COMPUTER-BASED FRESHMAN PHYSICS
LABORATORY EXPERIMENTS
SECOND EDITION

GOTTIPATY RAO

bluedoor
flexible & affordable learning solutions™

Chief Executive Officer: Jon K. Earl

President, College: Lucas Tomasso
President, Private Sector: Dawn Earl

Print Solutions Manager: Connie Dayton
Digital Solutions Manager: Amber Wahl
Content Solutions Manager: Anne Loyle-Langholz
Developmental & Production Coordinator: Meg Olstad
Senior Project Coordinator: Dan Woods
Senior Project Coordinator: Peggy Li
Project Coordinator: Erica Nilsen
Project Coordinator: Kelli Fleck
Project Coordinator: Andy Neidt
Project Coordinator: Kristin Bechthold
Production Assistant: Stephanie Larson
Production Assistant: Jessie Steigauf

Cover Design: Dan Woods

ISBN-13: 978-1-68135-046-2

© 2017 by Gottipaty Rao.

© Cover images by Shutterstock.

Published by bluedoor, LLC
              10949 Bren Road East
              Minneapolis, MN 55343-9613
              800-979-1624
              www.bluedoorpublishing.com

Printed in the United States of America.
10 9 8 7 6

TABLE OF CONTENTS

Section 1

Section 2

Section 3

Section 4

Section 5

Section 6

Section 7

Section 8

Section 9

Section 10

Section 11

Section 12

Section 13

Section 14

Section 15

Section 16

An appropriate laboratory experience is absolutely essential to learning the fundamentals of physics. With the availability of a wide range of powerful sensors along with computer software for online data acquisition, data processing, numerical calculations, and graphics, the physics laboratory experience can be very exciting while at the same time less time consuming in comparison to the traditional laboratory practice. The present laboratory manual in Mechanics provides, with such tools, the necessary framework, background, and methodology for a rich interactive laboratory experience. Since the sensor and computer based freshman laboratory equipment are now quite standard and commercially available, the experiments presented here can be universally implemented in almost all the instructional laboratories.

Each experiment presented in this laboratory manual is self-contained and in general has the following sub-sections: Introduction, Objectives, Theory, Experimental Details, Experimental Procedure, and Questions. The manual can be used as a stand-alone laboratory manual at the high school or freshman level for both calculus-based and algebra- and trig-based courses. Wherever applicable, required formulae are derived employing only algebra and trig, besides employing calculus-based methods.

The first chapter provides General Laboratory Information. In this chapter, detailed instruction on the preparation of the laboratory report and a discussion on error estimation and curve fitting procedures are presented. Writing a proper laboratory report is an important part of the laboratory experience. Through this particular exercise the student improves her/his technical writing and presentation skills.

Experiment 1 presents an introduction to electronic spreadsheets. From our experience, the introduction of electronic spreadsheets at the beginning of the laboratory course is quite useful. The students employ electronic spreadsheets for calculations, graphs, and to fit data to mathematical functions during the laboratory course. Many students found this experience to be quite helpful not only in the physics laboratory work and in solving physics problems, but in many other disciplines as well such as accounting, business, modeling, data manipulation and numerical methods, to name a few.

Three advanced level experiments have also been included:

- Anharmonic Oscillator – Simple Pendulum in Large Amplitude Oscillations (experiment # 32)
- Damped Harmonic Motion (experiment # 33)
- Longitudinal Oscillations of Two Coupled Masses (experiment # 34)

These experiments will be helpful to a motivated student who wishes to accomplish beyond the normal expectations of the course.

I have also included a number of experiments whose basic theme is the same but which have minor variations in the procedure or the equipment employed. One such example is: Measurement of the Coefficient of Static and Kinetic Friction. Such option enables an instructor to select an experiment of her/his choice; it also permits an instructor to choose an experiment that can be performed with the available equipment. In general, availability of a wider pool of experiments enables the instructor to coordinate the laboratory better with the lectures.

We have used this laboratory manual in our freshman laboratories for both Physics for Science Majors (calculus based) and College Physics (algebra and trig based) for more than 10 years and the student responses have been extremely positive and they seem to have really enjoyed the laboratory classes. We typically perform about 12 experiments in a semester. Many students have expressed that they would like to have more such laboratory experiments.

All the experiments presented in this manual have been performed in our freshman laboratory over many years; we have observed that they give reliable and reproducible results. If any instructor wishes to have additional details about the experiments or sample data, I will be happy to send them.

For the experiments in this manual, one may use either the software Logger Pro (Vernier Software & Technology, 13979 SW Millikan Way, Beaverton, OR 97005) or Capstone/Data Studio (PASCO, 10101 Foothills Blvd., Roseville, CA 95747). We have not made any systematic comparisons of the two software, but both are satisfactory for the freshman mechanics laboratory. The software can be loaded onto a PC or a MAC-based computer. In our freshman laboratory, we have been using the software for over fifteen years and we have found the performance and the reliability of the software good.

I am grateful to Brian Capozzi, and Binayak Kandel who have carefully read the manuscript and edited the chapters. My thanks are also due to Peggy Li for her attention to detail.

I would greatly appreciate comments and suggestions from the instructors and the students. They may please be sent to G. N. Rao, Department of Physics, Adelphi University, Garden City, NY 11530, or email: rao@adelphi.edu.

Gottipaty N. Rao
Garden City, NY

General Laboratory Information

I. Introduction to the Laboratory

Why Laboratory Experience?

Experiments play a pivotal role in our understanding of the physical world, the universe, and the laws that govern them. No law or theory can be acceptable unless its predictions are confirmed by experiments.

In this laboratory, you will be introduced to the so-called scientific methods on how to plan an experiment, interpret collected data, and estimate and minimize errors. You will be asked to draw realistic conclusions from the data you have collected.

In the lectures, you will be learning a number of physics laws governing the motion of objects and the agencies that are responsible for their motion. You will have an opportunity to verify some of these laws in the laboratory to have a better appreciation and understanding of them.

All the experiments you will be conducting in this laboratory have been done in different laboratories many times before. Though you may not expect any exciting new results, you do get results that are specific to the experimental setup you used and the methodology you adapted. For each experiment, you will present the experimental results, analysis of the data and the conclusions drawn in the form of a laboratory report. In science and technology, presenting the experimental results involves important skills. The laboratory report will test your skills in technical writing and presenting the scientific and technical data.

You will be working with a number of modern gadgets such as sensors, and state-of-the-art on-line data acquisition and analysis techniques. Modern gadgets and computers provide you a rich laboratory learning experience without heavy demands on your time. You may invest the savings on your time in learning new things, exploring new ideas and concepts, or spend it in other productive ways. Computers will save you lot of time in data collection, data analysis, calculations and curve fitting.

In spite of the automation and computerization, you are expected to know all the experimental details of each experiment. The instructor will carefully assess you in the way you perform the experiment, and handle the equipment. The instructor may also ask you a number of questions related to the experiment, the principles involved and the experimental procedures.

Pre-laboratory Preparation

The students are strongly advised to read the necessary theory and the procedure well before the beginning of the experiment. Also, they are expected to understand clearly the data collection procedures and the details about the data analysis. The students often underestimate the importance of pre-laboratory preparation.

Laboratory Practice

The safety of all the personnel working in the laboratory is most important. Handle the equipment carefully so that you may not harm yourself or others in the laboratory. Read the necessary safe handling procedures and the instructions for the particular instrument/s. The instructor will detail the necessary safety procedures. Follow them carefully- no exceptions!

Handling the Equipment

Some of the equipment you will be handling is quite delicate. You should exercise care in handling the equipment in general, particularly when working with the electronic equipment and sensors. Additional details will be given in the text and by the instructor. You should be cautious in handling the electronic equipment that run on mains.

Laboratory Reports

You will submit a laboratory report for each experiment you have performed. The text part of the laboratory report should be neatly typed. No handwritten reports will be accepted. You are expected to perform most of the calculations using the computer. A computer printout giving the details of the calculations should be submitted along with each laboratory report. However, part of the report containing calculations may be handwritten.

The laboratory report may preferably be presented in the following format:

1. Experiment #, (left hand top corner of the first page)
2. Date on which the experiment was performed and the date on which the laboratory report was submitted (left hand top corner of the first page following experiment #)
3. Title of the experiment at the center of the page. Use larger font
4. Give your name, course #, course title and section followed by the name of your instructor. If you have done the experiment in a group, give the names of the partners as well.
5. Objectives of the experiment
6. Brief experimental procedure
7. Experimental data
8. Calculations
9. Experimental uncertainties
10. Relevant functional relationships (if applicable) and graphical plots
11. Conclusions
12. Answers to questions

In your laboratory report, avoid duplicating the text already provided in the write-up of the lab manual. Include, in your own words, what you intend to investigate and the principles involved, brief details of the experimental procedure and detailed calculations. If you have collected the data manually, submit the data sheets along with the lab report. If you have used the computer for calculations and graphical analysis, appropriate printouts should also be included in the report. Even though you might have performed the experiment in a group of 2-3 students and collected the data together, each member of the group will do the calculations, plots, answers to the questions, and conclusions independently and submit his/her report. If you are not able to complete the calculations during the lab period, you may save your data on your own floppy/CD or send the data as an attachment to your email. Any data left on the hard drive of the lab computer will be erased. If you have done the experiment in a group, you print out multiple copies or may submit copies of the computer data and computer plots.

The laboratory report should be reasonably self- contained so that any physicist who is familiar with the experiment would be able to understand the methodology you followed, the calculations you have carried out and the conclusions you have drawn.

II. Experimental Uncertainties (Errors in a Measurement)

Analysis of Experimental Data

In any experiment, you can measure a quantity only to a certain precision, often decided by the equipment used and a number of random phenomena such as power fluctuations. In this laboratory, you will be measuring a number of physical quantities such as acceleration due to gravity and you will be verifying a number of laws of physics such as conservation of momentum. If the quantity you are measuring was already measured a number of times employing higher precision techniques than available to you, then you know the true or accepted value. The *accuracy* of your measurement is a measure of how close your measured value is to the true or expected value. Independently you are also expected to estimate the uncertainties in your measurement. The estimated uncertainty in your measurement gives the precision of your measurement. You will present the absolute precision in the same units as the result. The relative precision is the ratio of the absolute precision and the result (both should be in the same units). Whenever applicable, you will present the inaccuracies in your measurements. It is necessary that every measured value should be reported along with the uncertainties involved. The experimental values have no true meaning unless they are presented with the estimated uncertainties. The estimated uncertainties also enable you to give your result to an appropriate significant digit. In the following, a brief introductory discussion on errors, propagation of errors, and procedures to estimate and minimize the errors is presented.

Kinds of Errors

Experimental errors may, in general, be classified as (1) systematic errors and (2) random or statistical errors. The mistakes you make while calculating values and reading instruments are not errors but are blunders/mistakes.

SYSTEMATIC ERRORS

Systematic errors are associated with the equipment used for the measurements. These errors can be caused by an incorrectly graduated ruler, an improperly zeroed multi-meter, an un-calibrated thermometer, a worn-out screw gauge, un-calibrated gates (in the case of computer based data acquisition) etc. You can, in principle, correct the equipment for systematic errors, but the procedures involved are tedious and time consuming. For example, if you wish to calibrate a thermometer, you have to immerse it in melting ice at normal pressure and check whether it reads 0°C (32°F) or not. Similarly, you will immerse it in boiling pure water at normal pressure and verify whether it reads 100°C (212°F) or not. If you find that the graduations on the thermometer are not correct, you will develop a procedure to correct your observations. In this laboratory, we do not expect you to go into the calibration procedures. However, we do expect that you make an estimate of the systematic errors. In general, the systematic errors tend to push the experimental observations consistently higher or lower and often you can easily identify them. Mostly, the systematic errors are more dominating compared to random errors and therefore you will do a careful analysis to identify and estimate them. When a series of measurements are performed, systematic errors result in values that are consistently higher or lower depending on the situation. Systematic errors may also be significant if you neglect some variable/s in an experiment. If you use an approximate value for a constant, which is used in a set of repeated measurements, you can identify this as a systematic error.

In this laboratory, you are expected to identify the sources of systematic errors in your experiment and comment on how these errors could have possibly affected your result.

RANDOM ERRORS

Random or statistical errors are due to unknown error contributions to the experiment; in fact, any error that fluctuates randomly falls in this category. These include judgment errors of the observer, unpredictable errors due to fluctuations in line voltage, temperature of the room, mechanical disturbances in the room etc. These errors are of random nature and can be estimated and minimized employing statistical procedures described later in this section.

The random errors can be minimized but cannot be eliminated altogether no matter how hard you try. Improving the quality of the equipment can reduce random errors. Incorporating a voltage regulator may reduce fluctuations in the mains, but the fluctuations cannot be completely eliminated. Random or statistical errors fluctuate randomly and can be estimated by repeating the same measurement several times. Random errors show normal or Gaussian distribution. Suppose that you are measuring the direct current passing through a resistor. You applied a 10V DC from a DC power supply which operates on mains. Because of fluctuations in the mains, the DC output from the power supply will not be exactly 10V DC all the time, but instead it can be slightly more or slightly less. We assume that the fluctuations in the voltage are random and are given by the Normal or Gaussian distribution. The Normal or Gaussian distribution is symmetric. For example, if you make a large number of measurements, the probability for observing 9.5V is equal to the probability for observing 10.5V. A plot of the Gaussian distribution function is given in Fig. 1. The probability is plotted as a function of a dimensionless parameter, z. The quantity z measures the deviation from the mean value in units of the standard deviation, σ.

Gaussian Probability Distribution

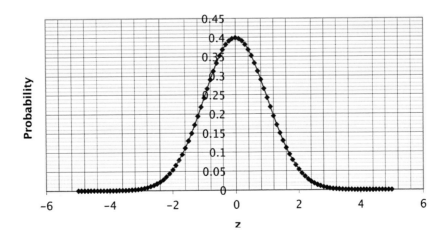

Figure 1.1 Gaussian probability distribution.

2.1 Mean is a Best Estimate of the True Value

Repeating the same measurement a number of times can reduce random or statistical errors. If x_1, x_2, ...x_n are the measured values of the same quantity you repeated n times, the mean (average) value of x is the sum of n determinations of x divided by n.

$$\overline{x} = \frac{x_1 + x_2 + x_3 + ... + x_n}{n} = \left(\frac{1}{n}\right)\sum_{i=1}^{n} x_i \tag{1.1}$$

Here, we assumed that all the measurements are equally reliable. From these measurements, you wish to find out the true value of the quantity x, which is unknown. It can be easily shown that the average is the best estimate of the true value of x.

As the number of times (n) you repeated a measurement increases, the value of x approaches the true value. It should be emphasized that systematic errors will not be affected by this procedure and only random or statistical errors will be minimized.

2.2 Precision of a Measurement

The precision of a measurement is the spread of results either relative to the average result or in absolute magnitude. The smaller the spread the better will be the precision.

For random errors, the precision of a measurement can be estimated by calculating the standard deviation of the measurements. First calculate the average value x, and then calculate the deviation of each of the measured value from the average value

$$\delta_1 = x_1 - \overline{x}$$

$$\delta_2 = x_2 - \overline{x}$$

$$\delta_n = x_n - \overline{x}$$

The average deviation

$$\delta = \frac{1}{n}\sum |x_i - \overline{x}| \tag{1.2}$$

gives the absolute value of the average dispersion of the measured values about the mean value $\overline{x}$

The standard deviation σ is the square root of the average of the squares of the deviations from the mean value

$$\sigma = \sqrt{\left(\frac{1}{n}\sum_{1}^{n}(x_i - \overline{x})^2\right)} \tag{1.3}$$

The variance, σ^2, is defined as the average of the squares of the deviation from the mean value, x.

$$\sigma^2 = (\delta_1^2 + \delta_2^2 + ... \delta_n^2)\left(\frac{1}{n}\right) \tag{1.4}$$

The above definitions are valid for infinite number of measurements, i.e. $n \rightarrow \infty$. However, when you collect a finite set of data such as you do in this laboratory, the standard deviation is better represented by

$$\sigma = \sqrt{\left(\frac{1}{n-1} \sum_{i}^{n}(x_i - \bar{x})^2\right)} \tag{1.5}$$

where we have used $(n-1)$ instead of n in Eq. (3). You will use Eq. (5) to calculate the standard deviation instead of Eq. (3).

The statistical errors have meaning only if you have repeated a particular measurement a number of times. The standard deviation gives the statistical uncertainty in the measured value. You will give the experimental result in the form

$$(\bar{x} \pm \sigma) \tag{1.6}$$

Where σ is the standard deviation.

In this analysis, we assumed that the errors follow a Normal or Gaussian probability distribution. Other probability distribution functions such as the binomial distribution and the Poisson distribution are employed in some experiments, but for most of the experiments you perform in this laboratory, the Gaussian or Normal distribution is applicable. The binomial distribution is applicable in situations where the result is one of a small number of final states such as tossing a coin or dice. The Gaussian or Normal distribution is an approximation to the binomial distribution when the number of possible outcomes is large and the probability of each outcome is finite. The Gaussian probability distribution function is a symmetric function about the mean value as shown in Fig. 1. In the Gaussian distribution the probability that an individual measurement falls within

$$(\bar{x} \pm \sigma)$$

is 68.3%. The probability that a measurement falls within

$$(\bar{x} \pm 2\sigma)$$

is 95.5%. The probability that a measurement falls within

$$(\bar{x} \pm 3\sigma)$$

is 99.7%.

2.3 Propagation of Errors (Uncertainties)

During laboratory work, you will be measuring a number of quantities (each having a certain uncertainty) and they are often used to calculate a certain other quantity of your interest. If you know the uncertainty in each of the measured quantities, what is the uncertainty in the quantity calculated?

You will first estimate the uncertainty in each measured quantity and then compute the uncertainty in the derived quantity. Let u and v be the measured quantities and σ_u and σ_v respectively be the corresponding standard deviations. Let z be the quantity calculated.

We assume that the dependent variable z is a function of measured quantities u and v

$$z = f(u, v) \tag{1.7}$$

Taking partial derivatives with respect to u and v,

$$\frac{\partial z}{\partial u} = \frac{\partial(u, v)}{\partial u} \quad and \quad \frac{\partial z}{\partial v} = \frac{\partial f(u, v)}{\partial v}$$

The variance

$$\sigma_z^{\,2} = \sigma_u^{\,2}\left(\frac{\partial f}{\partial u}\right)^2 + \sigma_u^{\,2}\left(\frac{\partial f}{\partial u}\right)^2 + 2\sigma_{uv}^{\,2}\left(\frac{\partial f}{\partial u}\right)\left(\frac{\partial f}{\partial v}\right)$$

We assume that u and v are uncorrelated so that the covariant term $\sigma_{uv} = 0$. The variance

$$\sigma_z^{\,2} = \sigma_u^{\,2}\left(\frac{\partial f}{\partial u}\right)^2 + \sigma_u^{\,2}\left(\frac{\partial f}{\partial u}\right)^2 \tag{1.8}$$

where σ_z is the standard deviation in z. In the following, we will develop some simple formulae to calculate the standard deviation in the derived quantity z, from the measured quantities using Eq. (8). For a detailed discussion on the propagation of errors, the reader is advised to refer Bevington and Robinson[1].

1. ADDITION AND SUBTRACTION OF AN INTEGER

If you add or subtract a positive integer a, to a measured quantity u and calculate a quantity z such that

$$z = u \pm a$$

Taking partial derivatives with respect to u

$$\frac{\partial z}{\partial v} = 1$$

The uncertainty in the calculated value z is equal to the uncertainty in the value of u. Therefore,

$$\sigma_z = \sigma_u \tag{1.9}$$

However, the relative uncertainty in z and u would be different. The relative uncertainty in z will be

$$\frac{\sigma_z}{z} = \frac{\sigma_z}{u \pm a}$$

whereas, the relative uncertainty in u is

$$\frac{\sigma_u}{u}$$

2. SUM

If you calculate z from the measured quantities u and v such that

$z = u + v$

Taking partial derivatives

$$\frac{\partial z}{\partial u} = 1 \quad \text{and} \quad \frac{\partial z}{\partial v} = 1$$

$$\sigma_z = \sigma_u^2 + \sigma_v^2 + 2\sigma_{uv}^2$$

Neglecting the covariant term σ_{uv},

$$\sigma_z = \sqrt{\sigma_u^2 + \sigma_v^2} \tag{1.10}$$

3. DIFFERENCE

If u and v are measured quantities and z is the dependent variable

such that

$z = u - v$

the uncertainty in the value of z is given by

$$\sigma_z = \sqrt{\sigma_u^2 + \sigma_v^2} \tag{1.11}$$

4. ADDITION AND SUBTRACTION

If the dependent variable z is expressed in terms of the measured quantities, u and v, such that

$z = au \pm bv$

Where a and b are constants.

Taking partial derivatives

$$\frac{\partial z}{\partial u} = a \quad \text{and} \quad \frac{\partial z}{\partial v} = \pm b$$

Neglecting the covariant term, the standard deviation in z is

$$\sigma_z = (a^2 \sigma_u^2 + b^2 \sigma_v^2)^{1/2} \tag{1.12}$$

5. MULTIPLICATION

Let u and v are the measured quantities and the dependent variable z is expressed by an equation of the type

$z = \pm\, auv$ where a is a constant.

Taking partial derivatives

$$\frac{\partial z}{\partial u} \pm av \quad \text{and} \quad \frac{\partial z}{\partial v} \pm au$$

$$\sigma_z^2 = (av\sigma_u)^2 + (au\sigma_v)^2$$

Here, we neglected the covariant term. The standard deviation in z is given by

$$\sigma_z = [(av\sigma_u)^2 + (au\sigma_v)^2]^{1/2} \tag{1.13}$$

6. DIVISION

If the dependent variable

$$z = \pm a\frac{u}{v}$$

where u and v are measured quantities and a is a constant. Taking partial derivatives

$$\frac{\partial z}{\partial u} = \pm\frac{a}{v} \quad \text{and} \quad \frac{\partial z}{\partial v} = \mp\frac{au}{v^2}$$

The variance

$$\sigma_z^2 = \left[\frac{a^2\sigma_u^2}{v^2} + \frac{a^2 u^2 \sigma_v^2}{v^4}\right]$$

$$\sigma_z^2 = z^2 \left[\frac{\sigma_u^2}{u^2} + \frac{\sigma_v^2}{v^2}\right]$$

Here, we have neglected the covariant term.

The standard deviation in z

$$\sigma_z = \left[\frac{a^2\sigma_u^2}{v^2} + \frac{a^2 u^2 \sigma_v^2}{v^4}\right]^{1/2} \tag{1.14}$$

7. POWERS

(a) If the derived quantity z is obtained by raising the measured value u to a power such that

$$z = au^{\pm b}$$

Where a and b are constants. Taking the derivative of z with respect to u

$$\frac{\partial z}{\partial u} = \pm abu^{\pm b-1} = \pm \frac{bz}{u}$$

The standard deviation in z

$$\sigma_z = \pm bz\frac{\sigma_u}{u} \tag{1.15}$$

(b) If the value of z is obtained by raising a constant, a, to a power of the measured quantity u

$$z = a^{\pm bu}$$

Where a and b are constants. Taking the derivative of z with respect to u

$$\frac{\partial z}{\partial u} = \pm zb \ln a$$

Where ln is the natural logarithm. The standard deviation in z

$$\sigma_z = \pm(zb \ln a)\,\sigma_u \tag{1.16}$$

8. EXPONENTIALS

If the dependent variable z is obtained by taking the exponential of a measured quantity u such that

$$z = ae^{\pm bu}$$

where a and b are constants.

Taking the derivative of z with respect to u

$$\frac{\partial z}{\partial u} = \pm abe^{\pm bu} = \pm bz$$

The standard deviation in z

$$\sigma_z = \pm bz\,\sigma_u \tag{1.17}$$

9. LOGARITHMS

If the dependent variable, z, is obtained by taking the logarithm of a measured quantity u

$z = a \ln (u)$

Where a and b are constants.

Taking the derivative of z with respect to u

$$\frac{\partial z}{\partial u} = \frac{a}{u}$$

The standard deviation in z

$$\sigma_z = \frac{a \, \sigma_u}{u} \qquad\qquad\qquad (1.18)$$

EXAMPLE 1

Suppose that you are interested in calculating the volume of a right circular cylinder. You measured the radius r and the uncertainty in the radius measurement is Δr. The measured value of its height is h and the uncertainty in the height measurement is Δh. What is the uncertainty ΔV in the calculated value of the volume V?

$V = \pi r^2 h$

$V = V(r, h)$

The partial derivatives of V with respect to r and h give

$$\frac{\partial V}{\partial r} = 2\pi \, r \, h, \qquad \frac{\partial V}{\partial h} = \pi r^2$$

The equations give the fractional uncertainty in V resulting from the uncertainties in r and h. The total error, ΔV, in V is

$$\Delta V \approx \frac{\partial V}{\partial r} \Delta r + \frac{\partial V}{\partial h} \Delta h$$

Where we have neglected the covariant term.

$\Delta V \approx 2\pi r h \, \Delta r + \pi r^2 \Delta h$

You will calculate the value of ΔV the error in V using the uncertainities Δr and Δh in the measured values of r and h and give your final result as

Volume $= V \pm \Delta V$

The fractional uncertainty in V is given by:

$$\frac{\Delta V}{V} = \frac{2\Delta r}{r} + \frac{\Delta h}{h}$$

$$\Delta V = V\left[\frac{2\Delta r}{r} + \frac{\Delta h}{h}\right]$$

Since you know the values of all the quantities on the right hand side of the equation, you can estimate the uncertainty ΔV, the error in V.

Significant Digits

Any physical quantity you measure in a laboratory has a finite precision. The precision of a measurement depends on the instrument used and the number of times a measurement of the same quantity is repeated. Employing the procedure detailed in the preceding section, one can estimate the uncertainties and hence the precision of a measurement. When you present the results of your measurement, the final value should be rounded off to the significant digit depending on the precision of your measurement. In general, you are expected to present the final experimental result to an appropriate significant digit along with the uncertainties involved.

The accuracy of a measurement is determined by how close the measured value is compared to the accepted value. When you measure a certain quantity in a laboratory, only certain digits are significant. The significant digits of a measured quantity include all the numbers that are read on the instrument and one estimated fraction of the smallest division. If you measured the length of an object using a meter stick graduated in cm and mm, you will give your result in cm up to two decimal places. The first digit after the decimal is a measured one whereas the second digit is an estimated one. When you use a meter stick for measuring the length and give your result in cm, giving the result beyond the second digit after the decimal is wrong. It is mandatory that you give your result rounded off to the significant digit.

Suppose that you measured the length of a pencil using a meter stick as 2.45 cm. Here, you are certain about 2 cm and also 4 mm, whereas the last digit, 5, is an estimated one because the instrument used is graduated in mm only. You are not certain about the last digit because it is an estimated value and is subjective. Here, you measured the length to three significant digits. How do you present the data such that you convey to the people that you have measured the length to only 3 significant digits? You can write this number as 2.45 cm; 0.0245 m; 0.000 0245 km; 24.5 mm; or 24.5 x 10^3 µm. However, you should not give the result as 2.450 cm, or 24500.0 µm (1 m = 10^6 µm = 10^3 mm) because here you are claiming 4 and 5 significant digits respectively. If you had used a vernier caliper of least count 0.01 cm to measure the length of the same object, and if you have gotten 2.450 cm, then all the four digits are significant. If you had used a screw gauge of least count 0.001 cm, you would have been able to measure the length to five significant digits. As you employ higher precision equipment, the precision of the measurement is improved. However, it should be added that no measurement is perfect, and every measurement has uncertainties depending on the instrument used.

EXAMPLE 2

Suppose that you measured the length of a small piece of chalk as 2.30 cm using a meter scale.

You may express this quantity in a number of ways:

2.30 cm, 0.0230 m, 0.0000230 km, 23.0 mm, 23.0 x 10^3 μm.

1. The left most nonzero digit (2 in Example 2) is the most significant digit. The zeroes to the left of 2 will not be counted. This rule is applicable whether the number is an integer or has a decimal point.

2. If there is no decimal point (i.e., if the number is an integer) the right most nonzero digit is the least significant digit.

3. If the number has a decimal point, the right most digit (including zero) is the least significant digit, for example, 0 in 0.0230 m.

4. All the digits located between the least significant digit and the most significant digit are significant digits.

In order to conform to the rules stated above, in some cases you may have to express your result in scientific notation. In the example above, you may express the result as 23.0 x 10^3 μm and not as 23000 μm. Though the error propagation is better described by the methods described in section 2.3, the following procedure based on the significant digits also gives approximately similar results.

1. ADDITION AND SUBTRACTION

The number of significant digits in a measurement gives the precision with which the measurement is carried out. If you are adding or subtracting two or more quantities, the resulting quantity will have the smallest number of significant digits of all the numbers used in the calculation. For example, if you are adding the following numbers: 2.3 (having 2 significant digits) and 2.30 (having 3 significant digits), the result will be 4.6 (having 2 significant digits) and not 4.60 (having 3 significant digits).

2. MULTIPLICATION

When you multiply two or more quantities, the final answer in general will have significant digits equal to the least number of significant digits of the numbers multiplied.

Example

6.3 x 5.**2** = 32.**76**

The result is **33**. Here the uncertain digits are given in the boldface and the least significant digit is rounded off. The result should include only the first doubtful digit. The result should not be given as 32.7**6** or 32.**76**.

EXAMPLE 3

25 x 5 = 125= **1**. 3 x 10^2. The result should not be given as 125.

3. DIVISION

In the division of two or more numbers, the number of significant digits in the answer is, in general, equal to the least number of significant digits in the measurements. If you divide a number 256 having 3 significant digits (**6** is the doubtful digit) by a number 15 having two significant digits (**5** is the doubtful digit)

$$256/15 = 17.066\ldots\ldots$$

The result will have only two significant ant digits. The resulting number, 17.066 , will be rounded off as 17. Here, 1 is the significant digit and **7** is the doubtful digit.

4. ROUNDING OFF NUMBERS

If you have a number with 3 significant digits, you will round off the fourth digit. If the digit being rounded off is 5 or more than 5, the preceding digit is incremented by 1. If the digit being rounded off is 4 or less; the preceding digit will be unaffected. If you are rounding off 6.237 to 3 digits, the result will be 6.24.

5. ADDITION OF NUMBERS

In the addition process, identify the doubtful rightmost digit, round off all the numbers to this digit, and then add.

Example: if you wish to add the following numbers (the doubtful digit is given boldface)

26.8**2**

521.92**3**

0.236**7**

4.**3**

You will round off all the numbers to the first decimal place, add them and round off the result to the first decimal place. The numbers will be

26.8

521.9

0.2

4.3

the sum will be 553.**2**.

The result will be given to the first decimal place only.

Percent Accuracy

If you know the true or the accepted value, T, of a physical quantity you measured, you can estimate the fractional and percent accuracy. If the measured value is M,

The absolute value of the difference $= |M - T|$

To get the absolute value, subtract the quantity T from M and ignore the sign if the result is a negative quantity. If $M = 26.1$ and $T = 28.3$, then $M - T = 26.1 - 28.3 = -2.2$. The absolute value of this is $+2.2$.

Fractional Accuracy = Absolute difference / True (accepted) value

$$= \frac{|M - T|}{T}$$

Percent Accuracy = Fractional Accuracy x 100%

III.   Graphical Representation of Data

In the laboratory, you will be investigating the functional relationships between a number of related quantities such as distance traveled as a function of time, velocity as a function of time etc . After collecting data on the related quantities, you will present the data in the form of graphs. Graphical presentation provides a clear visual picture of the functional dependence of the related quantities. You can also fit the data to an appropriate mathematical expression to establish the functional relationship and to provide the best estimates of the constants.

Though a variety of graphs may be plotted, in this course we are primarily interested in the $x - y$ scatter plots. The $x - y$ scatter plots give the relationship between two quantities; for example, distance traveled as a function of time. The related quantities are plotted employing a two dimensional Cartesian coordinate system (rectangular coordinates). The horizontal axis (x) is called abscissa and the vertical axis (y) the ordinate. Each data point is represented by its coordinates (x, y) in the $x - y$ plane. For the preparation of graphs, you will use the graphics program available with the Excel software. The following guidelines will be helpful in the preparation and presentation of the graphs.

1.   Label each axis with the quantity plotted and the values of the quantity at suitable intervals.
2.   Give the units of the quantities plotted.
3.   Give the title of the graph.
4.   See that the plot covers a good fraction of a page.
5.   All the labels and data points should be of sufficiently large in size so that one can read them with no ambiguity.
6.   If you have multiple plots in the same graph, give the legend for each plot.

Mathematical Functions to Fit Data

The functional relationship between quantities may be linear, quadratic, exponential, sinusoidal etc. In the following a brief discussion on the commonly employed functional relationships are presented.

1. LINEAR DEPENDENCE

If a quantity varies linearly with another quantity then the relationship is said to be linear. If y varies linearly with x, then y may be written as a constant m times x plus a constant. Algebraically, the relationship may be written as

$y = mx + c$

where c is a constant.

Examples

If a car is moving at a constant speed, the distance traveled is a linear function of time. For a homogeneous body, the mass is linearly proportional to the volume. If an object is moving with constant acceleration, the velocity is a linear function of time.

If you plot the related quantities in a two-dimensional Cartesian coordinate system, the relationship is represented by means of a straight line with a slope $(= m)$. The slope m $(=\Delta y/\Delta x)$ gives you the variation of y $(=\Delta y)$ with the variation of x $(=\Delta x)$ and will be a constant for a given straight line. The quantity c is the y-intercept when $x = 0$, which defines the initial condition.

2. QUADRATIC DEPENDENCE

During the laboratory work, you would notice that a number of physical quantities you will be dealing with have quadratic dependence. If you plot the related quantities, you would notice that the relationship is given by a parabola. Algebraically, the relationship may be written in the form

$Y = c_1 x + c_2 x^2$

where c_1 and c_2 are constants.

Examples

(a) If you drop a ball (initial speed equal to zero) from the roof of a building, the distance traveled d by the ball as measured from the roof of the building is related to time t

$d = c\, t^2$ or

$y = c\, x^2$

However, if you throw the ball vertically downwards with an initial velocity, then the distance traveled is given by

$d = c_1 t + c_2 t^2$

where c_1 and c_2 are constants.

(b) If you stretch a spring by a length x from its mean position, the potential energy stored in the spring is a quadratic function of x and may be expressed in the form

$PE = c\, x^2$ where c is a constant.

3. HYPERBOLIC DEPENDENCE

You notice that certain quantities are inversely proportional to each other. Their functional relationship may be written as

$$y = \frac{c}{x}$$

where c is a constant.

For example, if you are driving from San Francisco to Los Angeles ($d \sim 500$ miles) and if your average speed increases, the time taken for the trip decreases and vice versa. The time taken t is inversely proportional to the average speed v.

$$t = d/v$$

where d is a constant.

4. SINUSOIDAL DEPENDENCE

In this case, the functional dependence between the quantities is represented by a sine/cosine function. Mathematically, the relationship may be expressed as

$$x = a \sin (2 \pi f t + \varphi)$$

where x is the displacement, t is the time, a is the amplitude, f is the frequency, and φ is the phase. Here, the displacement is a sinusoidal function of time.

Examples

(a) Oscillations of a simple pendulum

The angular displacement of a simple pendulum for small amplitude oscillations is a sinusoidal function of time, t

$$\theta = \theta_0 \sin 2\pi f t$$

The angular displacement θ is a sinusoidal function of time t. The angular amplitude is θ_0 and the frequency is f.

(b) Oscillations of a mass attached to a spring

If you attach a mass to a spring, stretch the mass, and release it, you will find that the mass will be executing simple harmonic oscillations. The displacement of the mass with respect to its mean position may be expressed as

$$x = x_0 \sin 2\pi f t$$

The displacement x is a sinusoidal function of the time t. The amplitude is x_0 and the frequency is f.

If you use the value of $\pi = 3.141$, you will have the angle ($2 \pi f t$) in radians. Make sure your calculator is in the radians mode when you calculate the value of a trigonometric function. If you use the value of $\pi = 180°$, then the angle ($2 \pi f t$) is in degrees in which case your calculator should be in the degrees mode when you calculate the value of a trigonometric function.

5. LOGARITHMIC DEPENDENCE

Certain physical quantities have logarithmic dependence. Mathematically, the logarithmic dependence may be expressed as

$$y = c_1 \ln x + c_2$$

where c_1 and c_2 are constants and ln is the natural logarithm.

6. POLYNOMIAL DEPENDENCE

If y is a function of x, in general a polynomial dependence may be written as

$$y = c_1 + c_2 x + c_3 x^2 + c_4 x^3 \dots + c_7 x^6 + \dots$$

where $c_1, c_2, \dots$ are constants. The values of the different constants will decide the relative strengths of the different terms in the polynomial.

7. EXPONENTIAL DEPENDENCE

A number of physical quantities have exponential dependence of the type

$$y = c_1 e^{c_2 x}$$

Here, c_1 and c_2 are constants and e is the base of natural logarithm.

8. POWER DEPENDENCE

Some physical quantities have a power dependence of the type

$$y = c x^n$$

where c and n are constants.

Method of Least Squares

Often, you measure quantities that are interrelated. For example, if you throw an object vertically downwards with an initial velocity v_0 the velocity of the object as a function of time may be expressed in the form

$$v(t) = gt + v_0$$

If you measure velocity $v(t)$ as a function of time t and plot $v(t)$ vs. t, you expect a linear dependence resulting in a straight-line curve of the form $y = mx + c$.

Here, $v(t)$ and t are measured quantities whereas g and v_0 are constants. The measured values of v(t) also depend on g and v_0. Since you have two unknown quantities (v_0 and g), you can determine them by taking two pairs of measurements and solving the two simultaneous equations.

If the measured values of $v(t)$ and t have no errors, the plot $v(t)$ versus t would be a perfect straight line. Its slope $dy/dx = dv/dt$ gives the acceleration due to gravity g and the y-intercept when $x = 0$ gives the value of the initial velocity v_0. However, the measured values of the velocity as well as the measured values of the time have experimental errors. Therefore the plotted data scatter about a true straight line. The smaller the errors, the smaller the scattering. Because of the scatter in the data, one can (in principle) draw numerous curves. For a given set of data how do we draw a curve that would give the correct functional relationship between the quantities involved? The method of least squares enables you to draw a unique curve. The least squares fitted straight line is drawn such that 'the sum of the squares of the deviations of the measured values from the predicted line is minimized'. Whenever you manually (without the aid of computers) draw a curve passing through the data points, you will draw the curve using the method of least squares. Similar procedures are followed employing the computers as well.

If x_i are the measured values, the most probable value of x is obtained by minimizing the quantity

$\Sigma(x - x_i)^2$ where x is the value on the fitted curve. The value of x is varied until you get a minimum of the sum $\Sigma(x - x_i)^2$.

From a practical point of view, according to the method of least squares, you may draw a straight line such that the line passes through the centroid (X_n, Y_n) of the points (x_1, y_1), (x_2, y_2) (x_3, y_3), ... (x_n, y_n). The equation of the straight line passing through the centroid may be written as

$$Y_n = mX_n + c$$

where

$$X_n = \frac{x_1 + x_2 + x_3 + ... + x_n}{n}$$

and

$$Y_n = \frac{y_1 + y_2 + y_3 + ... + y_n}{n}$$

The least squares fitted curve gives the best-fitted curve for a given data set. This plot would also give you the best estimate of the unknown quantities.

For Further Reading on Errors and their Propagation

1. T. G. Hughes and T. P. A. Hase, *Measurements and their uncertainties,* Oxford Unity Press, 2010.

2. P. R. Bevington and D. K. Robinson, *Data Reduction and Error Analysis for the Physical Sciences,* Third Edition, McGraw-Hill, 2003. (For additional details about error propagation, the reader is advised to read this book.)

3. N. C. Barford, *Experimental Measurements: Precision, Error and Truth,* Addison Wesley, 1967.

4. H. D. Young, *Statistical Treatment of Experimental Data,* McGraw-Hill, 1962.

Home Assignment

1. Consider a rectangular box of the following dimensions:

   Length = $l \pm \Delta l$, breadth = $b \pm \Delta b$, and the depth = $d \pm \Delta d$. The quantities Δl, Δb, and Δd are the uncertainties in the corresponding measurements. (a) What is the uncertainty, ΔV, in the calculated volume? (b) If the measured values are l = 1.235 ± 0.005 m, b = 0.532 ± 0.001 m and h = 2.362 ± 0.005 m, calculate the volume V and the uncertainty in the volume (ΔV).

2. You wish to calculate the volume of a sphere. You measured the radius of the sphere using a Vernier caliper as r = 2.35 ± 0.01 cm. Calculate the volume V in cubic meters and ΔV the uncertainty in V.

3. Mary is interested in measuring the DC voltage output of a power supply. Using a digital voltmeter, she repeated the measurement 10 times and the values are given below. Calculate the best value of the voltage and the standard deviation.

Measurement #	DC Voltage (Volts)
1	4.325
2	4.330
3	4.310
4	4.320
5	4.315
6	4.322
7	4.323
8	4.319
9	4.326
10	4.317

4. How many significant digits are there in the following?

   (a) 5.000   (b) 8.00 x 10^2 (c) 0.0040   (d) 0.003 x 10^6

5. Add the following numbers and give your result to the significant digit

   5.32**6**; 6.45**0**; 113.6**7**; 10.765**3**; 6.8**7**

   The significant digits are given in boldface.

6. Make a plot of the following data (d on y-axis and t on x-axis) and draw a least squares fitted curve. What can you conclude about the functional dependence of the quantities t and d? Write a simple mathematical relation expressing the functional relationship of the quantities t and d.

Time t (hours)	Distance d (miles)
1	11
3	38
5	57
6	75
8	93
12	138
15	180
18	212
22	257

Introductory Experiments

Experiments 1 & 2

I.   Introduction and Objectives

The electronic spreadsheets have emerged as powerful tools to perform a number of calculations, data collection and analysis, build models, and prepare graphical plots in science, business, engineering, accounting etc. Using them, one can build dynamic models without learning formal languages. The electronic spreadsheets are convenient to manipulate and plot the data, fit the data to an equation and explore the functional relationships readily. You are introduced to the electronic spreadsheets in the beginning of this course so that you may conveniently use them in the laboratory for data analysis and in the physics tutorials to solve problems.

OBJECTIVE

Get familiar with the Excel Software for data collection and analysis and study the functional relationships between the related quantities employing graphs. During the laboratory period, you will reproduce the four worked out examples along with the plots. If you are already familiar with the electronic spreadsheets, you may work on the home assignment problems during the class period.

II.   Equipment

A PC or Mac loaded with Microsoft Excel software.

III. Introduction to Electronic Spreadsheets (Microsoft Excel)

Excel Screen/Worksheet

Click on Start, Programs and Microsoft Excel. You will be opening an Excel worksheet. The worksheet (Fig. 2.1) consists of a large number of columns and rows. Each column is represented by a letter and each row by means o f a number. The intersection of a column and a row is called a cell and is identified by the letter of the column followed by the row number. For example, the intersection of column C and row 8 is the cell C8. You may enter in any cell a comment, a number or a mathematical formula.

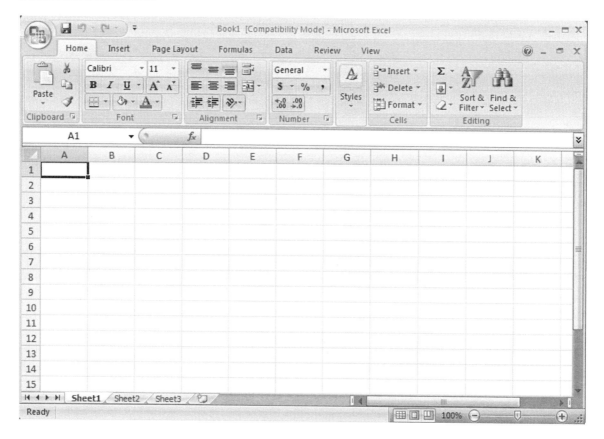

Figure 2.1: Excel spreadsheet

The first line is called the Title Bar with the software title "Microsoft Excel". On the right end are the buttons Minimize, Restore, and Close.

The second line is called the Ribbon. It displays the application menus.

RIBBONS

Home, Insert, Page Layout, Formulas, Data, Review, and View

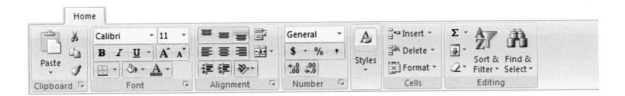

Home: You can change the font type and size, cut, copy and paste. Similarly you can change the alignment of the texts, format numbers and format cells. Moreover, you can also change font color, insert and delete cells, rows, and columns.

Insert: You can insert pictures, shapes and clip art. Similarly you can also insert charts and graphs, different symbols, pictures, different shapes, text box, header and footer. You can make bar graph, pie chart, scatter plot diagram, and other different types of graphs.

Page Layout: You can change the themes like colors, fonts, and effects of your page. Similarly you can change page setup. You can change the margin of paper and the type of paper like legal, letter, etc. You can also change the dimensions of header and footer.

Formulas: You can insert different functions of your own as well as all the functions available in the Excel software. If you want to write your own function, you can do that but you have to type it on the formula bar which is shown in Fig: 2.1.

Data: Using this tab you can import data from external sources like web, excess and text. Similarly you can also sort data in ascending or descending order and from A through Z or vice versa. Moreover, you can also make a group of data and get subtotal of only that group of data.

Review: Using this tab you can check spelling, access Thesaurus, Protect Sheet, Protect Workbook, Share Workbook etc.

View: Using this tab, you can view Page Layout, Page Break Preview, Custom Views, Ruler, Gridlines, Formula Bar, Headings, Zoom, Macros etc.

At the bottom of the worksheet is a **Tab** to identify the worksheets. You may use **Sheet 1, Sheet 2,** etc. to enter data of different categories and perform calculations.

Scroll arrows: The arrows are at each end of the scroll bar. You click on them with the mouse to move through your worksheet one row or one column at a time.

Scroll boxes: They show the current relative position of the active cell. By dragging the scroll boxes with the mouse, you can scroll through the document.

Use of the Mouse: You can move around the screen using either keyboard commands or the mouse. With the help of the mouse, you can quickly move around the screen, select cells, give commands, and insert data and formulae easily. While entering formulae, using the mouse is less prone to mistakes. We will restrict our discussion to the use of the mouse.

Entering/Deleting/Editing Information

SELECTING A CELL

Point to the cell and left click the mouse.

Any cell may be used for *label* (entering explanatory text) or *value or formula*. Click on the cell in which you wish to enter the information. As you type, the entries will be shown in the cell as well as in the formula bar. The formula bar displays the current Address (cell identification) and the contents of the current cell. If the text is more than the width of the cell, the text will spill over to the next cells if they are empty. The formula bar displays the cell reference, cancel (X), and enter ($\sqrt{}$) boxes and the data in the current cell. You can insert or modify data or formula with the help of the insertion point. The insertion point is a vertical bar which can be moved with the help of the cursor.

LABELS, VALUES AND FORMULAE

1. *Labels* provide explanations, titles, identify the entries in a cell, column, row etc., and a host of other information which is not directly used in the calculations. To label, you simply mark the cell, enter the information and press **enter** on the keyboard or click the **enter** box. The information may extend beyond the cell length and into the other cells, if other cells are empty. You should be careful that the text and the value that will be used for calculations should not be mixed and entered in the same cell.

2. *Values* are data that can be used for modeling and or calculations. To enter a value you mark the cell, enter the data and **enter** or click the **enter** box

3. *Formulae* are employed for calculations. The formulae must be entered in the spreadsheet format. The cells containing formulae normally display the calculated result rather than the formulae. However, the formula can be accessed by clicking on the appropriate cell when the formula is displayed in the window.

ENTERING DATA

There are different ways to enter data in Excel: in an active cell or in the formula bar.

To enter data in an **active cell**:

- Click in the **cell** where you want the data

- Enter Data and press **enter** on the keyboard or click the **enter** box.

To enter data into the **formula bar**

- Click the cell where you would like the data

- Place the cursor in the **Formula Bar**

- Type your own formula in the Excel format or click on the built in formula in the Excel data base

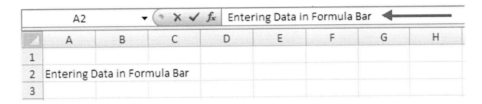

SELECT DATA

To select a cell or data to be copied or cut:

- Click on the cell

- Click and drag the cursor to select many cells in a range

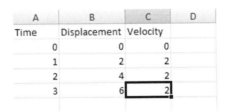

SELECT A ROW OR COLUMN

- To select a row or column click on the **row** or **column header**.

COPY AND PASTE

To copy and paste data:

- Select the cell(s) that you wish to copy
- On the **Clipboard** group of the **Home** tab, click **Copy**
- Select the cell(s) where you would like to copy the data
- On the **Clipboard** group of the **Home** tab, click **Paste**

CUT AND PASTE

To cut and paste data:

- Select the cell(s) that you wish to copy
- On the Clipboard group of the Home tab, click Cut
- Select the cell(s) where you would like to copy the data
- On the Clipboard group of the Home tab, click Paste

UNDO AND REDO

To undo or redo your most recent actions:

- On the **Quick Access Toolbar**
- Click **Undo** or **Redo**

Copy

Paste

Cut

Undo

AUTO FILL

The Auto Fill is an important feature of the Excel software. If you entered a formula in a cell and if you wish that the operation repeated for several other cells in a relative manner, this feature will be extremely useful. To use the Auto Fill feature:

- Click on the cell. Fill Handle shows up at the right hand bottom of the cell with a + sign
- Drag the Fill Handle to complete the cells

INSERT CELLS, ROWS, AND COLUMNS:

To insert cells, rows, and columns in Excel:

- Place the cursor in the row below where you want the new row, or in the column to the left of where you want the new column
- Click the **Insert** button on the **Cells** group of the **Home** tab. Alternatively right click on the cells which will show a pop up menu. Click on the option of your interest.
- Click the appropriate choice: **Cell, Row**, or **Column**

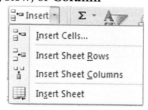

INSERT, SYMBOLS AND SPECIAL CHARACTERS

- Click on **INSERT**, **Symbol**, highlight the symbol you wish to insert and click on **Insert**.

DELETE CELLS, ROWS AND COLUMNS

To delete cells, rows, and columns:

- Place the cursor in the cell, row, or column that you want to delete
- Click the Delete button on the Cells group of the Home tab. Alternatively you may right click on the high-lighted cells and follow the optins in the popup menu.
- Click the appropriate choice: Cell, Row, or Column

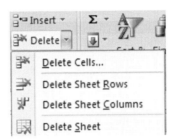

EXCEL FORMULAS

A formula is a set of mathematical instructions that can be used in Excel to perform calculations. Formals are entered in the formula box with an = sign.

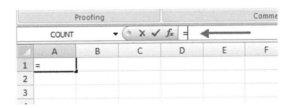

There are many elements to an excel formula.

 References: The cell or range of cells that you want to use in your calculation
 Operators: Symbols (+, -, *, /, etc.) that specify the calculation to be performed
 Constants: Numbers or values that do not change
 Functions: Predefined formulas in Excel

To create a basic formula in Excel:

- Select the **cell** for the formula
- Type = (the equal sign) and the **FORMULAS, Insert Function,** select **Category** and select a **Function** and click **OK**
- Click **Enter**

CALCULATE WITH FUNCTIONS

Of particular interest is the **Function** under the main menu **Insert**. This would enable you to insert a variety of built – in functions. You can insert function of the type SIN( ) , COS( ), SUM ( ), etc. employing this feature.

A function is a built in formula in Excel. A function has a name and arguments (the mathematical function) in parentheses. For example, the functions in Excel:

Sum: Adds all cells in the argument
Average: Calculates the average of the cells in the argument
Min: Finds the minimum value
Max: Finds the maximum value
Count: Finds the number of cells that contain a numerical value within a range of the argument

To calculate a function:

- Click the **cell** where you want the function applied

- Click the **Insert Function** button

- Choose the function

- Click **OK**

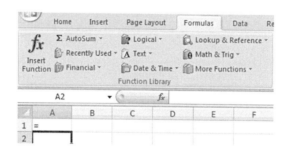

- Complete the Number 1 box with the first cell in the range that you wish to calculate

- Complete the Number 2 box with the last cell in the range that you want calculated

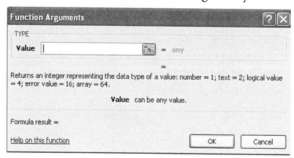

FUNCTION LIBRARY

The function library is a large group of functions on the **Formula Tab** of the Ribbon. These functions include:

AutoSum: Calculates the sum of a range
Recently Used: All recently used functions
Financial: Accrued interest, cash flow return rates and additional financial functions
Logical: And, If, True, False, etc.
Text: Text based functions

Date & Time: Functions calculated on date and time

Math & Trig: Mathematical Functions

More Functions: Statistical, Engineering, Cube, Information, Compatibility

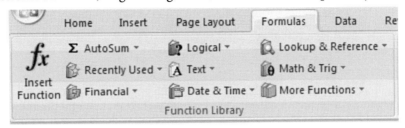

CREATE A CHART

To create a chart:

- Select the **cells** that contain the data you want to use in the chart

- Click the **Insert** tab on the Ribbon

- Click the type of **Chart** you want to create

- Most of the plots in this lab are scatter plots which will show the functional relationship between two quantities. First plot the data points (not the line plots) only. Right click on any data point, from the pop up menu click on **Add trend line**, then another pop menu shows up, choose the appropriate function. Click on **Display Equation** on chart and **Display R-squared value** on chart. If R-squared value is close to 1, the fit is good otherwise you will try other functions. Click on the **Axis** and choose **AXIS OPTIONS**. **Add Chart Title**. Right click any where on the chart, **CHART TOOLS** pops up. Left click on the **CHART ELEMENTS** and add **Chart Title, Axis Titles** and other elements as appropriate.

IV.   Calculations Using Excel Software

Entering a Formula

Formulae usually consist of a set of instructions to calculate the required quantities. In order to insert the formula in a given cell, place the insertion point in the cell and highlight it by clicking the mouse. Enter an equal sign (=) and then enter the formula using the Excel format. An equal sign indicates to the computer that you are not just entering the data but a formula and you want the computer to calculate the result for you. After completing entering the formula, press enter on the keyboard or click on the √ sign on the Formula Bar.

BASIC MATHEMATICAL OPERATIONS

Multiplication: *

Addition: +

Subtraction: -

Division: /

Exponentiation: ^

Colon: : (Denotes a range of cells)

For example, the formula in the cell E1

=A1+B1+D1

implies, add the contents of the cells A1, B1, and D1, and enter the result in the marked cell (E1).

When you use a formula to calculate a particular quantity, the result of the calculation is displayed in the cell (and not the formula). However, you can display the formula in the window (located just below the main menu) by highlighting the cell. You may also list a formula as a label in another cell (that is not used) with explanations so that you will have ready reference. Remember, when you label a cell, the equal sign (=) should not precede the information you want to enter.

When you want to change a formula already entered, you highlight the appropriate cell, bring the cursor to the required point on the formula bar and make the changes. After the changes, you press enter on the keyboard or click the enter ($\sqrt{}$) box.

Relative and Absolute Variables

A cell can make reference to another cell by: (1) absolute reference or (2) relative reference. An absolute reference always refers to a specific cell. It always reads the value in that specific cell for all the calculations.

A relative reference is a reference with respect to the location of that cell. Suppose you entered in D4 a formula = C4-B4. The program reads this relative reference as: read the contents of the cell located one row left of D4 and subtract the contents of the cell located two rows left of D4.

The absolute variables are those which do not change their values from cell to cell when a formula is copied or filled down. In contrast, relative variables change their address when a formula is copied or filled down. While entering a formula, it is an <u>absolute must</u> that you identify them accordingly. Otherwise, all your calculations will be messed up. If the data in cell F6 is an absolute variable, it will be entered as $F$6. The first $ sign indicates that it is an absolute variable with respect to the column and the second $ sign indicates that it is an absolute variable with respect to the row. Suppose that you are interested in calculating the velocity of an object thrown vertically upwards at time intervals $dt = 1s$. You wish to calculate the velocity at $t = 0$, $t = 1$, $t = 2$, $t = 3$ seconds etc. Here, t is a relative variable, whereas the increment in time, dt, is an absolute variable. You notice that the values of the absolute variables remain constant for the entire set of calculations.

Using 'Functions' of the Excel Software

Function in the context of the Excel software is an already designed formula. For example, SUM (B5:B12) gives you the sum of the cell values within the range of cells B5 to B12.

In the formula SUM (B5:B12), you do not have to type the addresses such as B5 and B12. Instead you may point the cursor at the cell B5 and click the mouse. You will notice that the appropriate cell Address is entered in the formula. This procedure is more intuitive, less prone to errors and saves considerable time. If you try to enter the cell number manually, you are more likely to make errors.

"What if" game

One of the advantages of the Excel program is its capability to play the "**what if**" game. When you change the value of a particular variable in a problem, the program automatically recalculates all the values using the new value of the variable. The power of this feature will be apparent when we solve some problems.

Suppose that you calculated the displacement as a function of time when a ball was thrown vertically upwards with an initial velocity of, say, 50 m/s. If you are interested to know how the displacement changes if the initial velocity is changed, you simply give a new value for v_0 and the Excel program recalculates all the values and even change the plots. This is a useful feature when you are studying the functional relationships in physics and other areas.

Fill Series

Enter the initial value of any series in any cell. Click on Restore on the right top corner on the Title bar so that you have a full screen of the application menus. Click on Fill on the Home menu You open a dialog window and enter the step value and the stop value and click on Rows/Columns, linear, growth, etc. as appropriate.

Format Cells

This feature is helpful when you wish to round off your calculations to a significant digit. Right click on the cell and from the pop up menu, choose Format cells, select number under the category and the significant digit. You can format whole column of data as well.

V.   Data Fitting Procedures Employing Excel Software

An x - y scatter plot gives the functional relationship between two quantities. Usually, x is the independent variable and y is the dependent variable. The functional relationship may be linear, quadratic, exponential, logarithmic, polynomial etc. In this course, whenever you make a plot, you are expected to fit the data to an appropriate mathematical expression and give the best fitted curve and the best fitted values.

In order to fit the data to a mathematical equation, right click on any data point on the plot, you will see a new pop up menu. Click on *Add Trend line* and select the desired option. You will see a set of six graphs on a dialog box. A brief discussion on these mathematical functions is given below.

Linear: Makes a least squares fit to an equation of the type
$$y = mx + c$$
where m is the slope and c is the y-intercept when $x = 0$

Go to options, you can select automatic fit or provide an equation and specify the intercept. Always click on display equation on chart and also click on display R-squared value on the chart. For most of the physics experiments, you will need this information for the analysis of the results.

Logarithmic: Makes a least squares fit to an equation of the type

$$y = c_1 \ln x + c_2$$

where c_1 and c_2 are constants and ln is the natural logarithm.

Polynomial: Makes a least squares fit to an equation of the type

$$y = c_1 + c_2 x + c_3 x^2 + c_4 x^3 \ldots + c_7 x^6$$

Here $c_1, c_2,\ldots$ are constants. You can also choose the order of the polynomial you wish to be fitted to the data.

Exponential: Makes a least squares fit to an equation of the type

$$y = c_1 e^{c_2 x}$$

where $c_1 \, c_2$ are constants and e is the base of natural logarithm.

Power: Makes a least squares fit to an equation of the type

$$y = c \, x^n$$

where c and n are constants.

Moving Average: Calculates the moving average over a specified period.

Custom Equation: You can also fit the data to a custom equation within the categories mentioned above. Click on *options-* and *custom-*, and type the equation in the space provided. You can also give the value of the intercept.

You have the options to display *equation on the chart* and *R-squared value on the chart. For most of the charts you prepare, you will choose these options and display the equation and the R-squared value on the chart.*

You click on the Chart Tools and then click on Design, and add the labels for the x- and y-axis as well as the chart title.

Insert Mathematical symbols, equations and Greek alphabets: Go to the Main Menu and insert, you will find a drop down menu on the right hand side.

Laboratory Report

Your laboratory report should include the home assignment problems worked out. You are expected to present Excel worksheets and plots for each of the problem. No details on the software or the procedures followed are necessary. You can also copy and paste the plots from the Excel worksheet to the Microsoft Word document. You will submit the home assignments with your lab report.

Examples: In the following, four worked-out examples are presented. They serve as model examples for the application of spreadsheets. If you are not familiar with the electronic spreadsheets, try to work out these examples during the class and the instructor will help you. The model solutions would be helpful in learning how to use Excel. If you are familiar with the electronic spreadsheets, you may do the home assignment problems during the class period.

EXAMPLE 1

Joe, who owns a convenient store purchased 10 items and sold them at a profit or loss. Calculate (1) net profit/loss and (2) average profit/loss.

Solution:

In any column, you will enter 'Item details'. In the model example provided, these data were entered in the cells A9 to A18. You could as well enter these data in the cells F22 to F31 or whatever. The cell A8 is used as 'label'. To enter labels, click the cell into which you want to enter the label, type the label and press enter on the keyboard or click the enter box. As you type, the entries will be shown in the cell as well as in the formula bar. (For additional details see section C). The labels are <u>not</u> employed for calculations.

The purchase prices are entered in a column cells B9 to B18. The purchase price may be entered in any column B, C, D ….but covering the rows 9 to 18. For entering the purchase price click on the cell, enter data and press enter key on the keyboard or click on the enter box. You will be using these data for calculations. <u>The cells that are used for the calculations should contain number only and should not be mixed with alphabets.</u>

Column C contains number of pieces purchased. These data will be used for the calculations.

Column D contains purchase cost. You will be calculating the cost per item from the cost per piece and the number of piece s purchased. In the cell D 9, you will be entering t h e formula used for calculation. First you click on the cell D9 and enter " = " sign. "Equal to" sign tells the computer t h at you are giving a formula in this cell and you want the computer to calculate the value using the formula give n in this cell and enter the result in this cell. You will enter =B9*C9 followed by pressing the enter key on the key board . The formula entered means : multiply the value in the cell B9 with the value in the cell C 9 and put the result back in the same cell.

You enter the data corresponding to the sale price in the cells E9 to E18. The column F deals with the sale proceeds. Since the sale price per piece was given in the column E, we wish to calculate the sale proceeds by multiplying the sale price by the number of pieces sold. In the cell F9, you will enter the formula "=E9*C9" followed by pressing the <u>enter</u> key on the keyboard.

The column G deals with profit/loss. In the cell G9, you enter the formula "=F9-D9" followed by pressing the enter key on the keyboard.

All the formulae you entered in this problem have been entered as relative variables (see the text for details). You wish to calculate the values in the cells D10 to D18, F10 to F18 and G10 to G18.

Since you have entered the formula in D9, you highlight the cell D9 and you will see a "+" sign at the right bottom of the cell. Click on the "+" sign and while keeping it pressed, drag the mouse to the cell D18. Follow similar procedure to fill the cells F9 through F18 and G9 through G18. You notice that the data in cell C10 is multiplied with the data in B10 and the result entered in D10. Similarly, the data in C11 is multiplied with the data in B11and the result entered in D11 and so on. When you want to highlight noncontiguous data/columns, you will keep the control key pressed while highlighting the cells of your interest. You will find that the computer has calculated the values you wanted and put them in the appropriate cells.

You wish to calculate the Net Profit/(Loss) and enter the data in the cell G1 9. Click on the cell G1 9 and enter =SUM(G9:G18) and press enter key. Equal to sign indicates that you are entering a formula. SUM is a built-in function in the Excel software meaning that you want the sum of the values in the cells G9 to G18. The colon indicates the beginning cell to the end cell in either rows or columns. Excel software has a number of built in functions, which can be inserted directly into a formula. Keep the cursor (vertical bar) at the appropriate place where you wish to enter the formula, go to Insert on the Menu bar, pull down menu and click on function. You will open a box with a number of built-in functions. Click on the function you need and it will be entered into the formula. For some functions, an interactive box will open, respond appropriately.

In cell G20, you wish to calculate the average profit/(loss). You will enter =AVERAGE(G9:G18) . AVERAGE is a built-in function, which can be entered directly where needed. If you are not sure whether some function is available or not, it may be a good idea to open the functions box and get familiar with them.

EXAMPLE 1

	A	B	C	D	E	F	G
1							
2							
3	Joe who owns a shop purchased 10 items and sold them at a profit or loss.						
4	Calculate (1) net profit/loss and (2) average profit/loss per item.						
5	Formula entered in cell D9 = B9*C9						
6	Formula entered in cell F9 = E9*C9						
7	Formula entered in cell G9 = F9-D9						
8	Item details	Purchased @	# of pieces	Cost of purchase ($)	Sale price @	Sale proceeds ($)	Profit/Loss ($)
9	#1	$ 1.35	20	$ 27.00	1.52	30.4	$ 3.40
10	#2	$ 2.56	15	$ 38.40	2.78	41.7	$ 3.30
11	#3	$ 5.89	55	$ 323.95	6.78	372.9	$ 48.95
12	#4	$ 0.91	24	$ 21.84	1.21	29.04	$ 7.20
13	#5	$ 0.85	67	$ 56.95	0.73	48.91	$ (8.04)
14	#6	$ 5.67	34	$ 192.78	6.29	213.86	$ 21.08
15	#7	$ 0.54	55	$ 29.70	0.34	18.7	$ (11.00)
16	#8	$ 0.65	39	$ 25.35	0.52	20.28	$ (5.07)
17	#9	$ 22.58	89	$ 2,009.62	21.69	1930.41	$ (79.21)
18	#10	$ 54.27	29	$ 1,573.83	57.98	1681.42	$ 107.59
19				Net profit/(loss)			$ 88.20
20				Average profit/(loss)			$ 8.82
21	Formula entered in cell G19 = SUM(G9:G18)						
22	Formula entered in cell G20 = AVERAGE(G9:G18)						
23	(1) When you want to enter data or explanation, click on the cell and enter						
24	(2) Alphabets should not be mixed with the numbers that are used for calculations.						
25	(3) The numbers that are used for calculations and the explanation should be entered in separate						
26	(4) When you want to do computations, you will click on the cell and enter the sign "=" and enter the formula						
27	When you have entered the formula, you press 'return' or click on						
28	(5) To calculate the cost of purchase, formula entered in cell D9 = B9*C9						
29	(6) To calculate the sale proceeds, formula entered in cell F9 = E9*C9						
30	(7) After you enter the formula in cell D9, high-light the cell D9, A + sign appears at the right hand bottom						
31	You point the cursor on the + sign and while keeping it pressed fill down to D18.						
32	You would notice that the data in C10 is multiplied with the data in B10 and the result entered in D10.						
33	Similarly the data in C11 is multiplied with the data in B11 and the result entered in D11.						
34	(8) To calculate the sum in cell G19, the formula entered = SUM(G9:G18). Here the colon in the						
35	parenthesis means that all the cells from G9 to G18 are to be added.						
36	(9) It is a good practice that you click on the appropriate cell using the mouse rather than entering the cell numbers						

EXAMPLE 2

Plot sin θ, cos θ, and tan θ for values of θ from 0° to 360° in increments of 10°.

Solution:
The angles are given in degrees. To calculate the sin, cos and tan values of the angle, first you have to convert the angles to radians. You know π radians is equal to 180°. Therefore to convert degrees to radians, you multiply the angle in degrees by π and divide by 180. π is a built-in function in Excel software as PI()(capital P, capital I). You can access this function and insert in the appropriate cell.

You can use any number of rows for explanations. This information will be useful to understand the details of the program you generated and in the future when you wish to make some changes in the program. The 8th row is used for labeling.

You wish to calculate the values of sin, cos and tan for angles 0 to 360° in increments of 10°.

- You will enter 0 in the cell A9. Nothing particular about column A, you can choose any column or any row. You enter in the cell A4, Δθ =
- You enter in the cell B4, 10
- You enter in the cell C4, degrees

As stated earlier, the values you will be using for calculations should not be mixed up with alphabets or symbols. You will be using 10 as an increment in degrees and therefore this number should be entered in a single cell. The explanations corresponding to this entry may be entered in any other cell/s.

- In the cell A10, you enter the formula =A9+$B$4 and press the enter key

Remember that the number10 is an absolute variable and not a relative variable (see the text for details). If the variable is an absolute variable both with respect to the row and the column such as the value 10 in the cell B4, you will indicate this by including a $ sign both before the row and the column of the cell where the data were entered as $B$4.

- Highlight the cell A10 when a + sign appears at the right bottom of the cell. Click the cursor on the + sign and drag through A45 to fill down. You will notice that the angles were incremented in10 degrees and the data were entered in the appropriate cells.
- In the cell B9, enter =SIN(A9*PI()/180) and press the enter key. The = sign indicates that you are entering a formula, SIN is a built-in function which calculates the sine values if the angles are given in radians, PI() is again a built-in function (=3.141...).
- In the cell C9 enter =COS(A9*PI()/180) and press enter key
- In the cell D9 enter =TAN(A9*PI()/180) and press enter key.
- Highlight the cells B9, C9 and D9 and Fill down through B45, C45, and D45. You will find that the sin, cos and tan values of the corresponding angles have been calculated and entered in the appropriate cells. For the plot purposes, you would like to delete the values corresponding to tan 90 and tan 270 degrees. The only reason is that these values are very large and you will not be able to display the functional dependence properly in a single graph.
- Highlight all the cells from A8 to D45. Click on the chart button, choose x-y scatter plot, choose a smooth curve with data points and finish the plots. You may label them appropriately as detailed in the text. If you prefer you may make two separate plots as done in the Example 2.

EXAMPLE 2

	A	B	C	D	E	F	G	H
1	Example 2							
2								
3	Plot Sinθ, cosθ, tanθ as a function of θ in degrees							
4	Δθ=	10	degrees	Formula entered in the cell A10 = A9+$B$4				
5	Formula entered in cell B9 = SIN(A9*PI()/180)							
6	Formula entered in cell C9 = COS(A9*PI()/180)							
7	Formula entered in cell D9 = TAN(A9*PI()/180)							
8	θ	sinθ	cosθ	tanθ				
9	0	0.0000	1.0000	0.0000				
10	10	0.1736	0.9848	0.1763				
11	20	0.3420	0.9397	0.3640				
12	30	0.5000	0.8660	0.5774				
13	40	0.6428	0.7660	0.8391				
14	50	0.7660	0.6428	1.1918				
15	60	0.8660	0.5000	1.7321				
16	70	0.9397	0.3420	2.7475				
17	80	0.9848	0.1736	5.6713				
18	90	1.0000	0.0000					
19	100	0.9848	-0.1736	-5.6713				
20	110	0.9397	-0.3420	-2.7475				
21	120	0.8660	-0.5000	-1.7321				
22	130	0.7660	-0.6428	-1.1918				
23	140	0.6428	-0.7660	-0.8391				
24	150	0.5000	-0.8660	-0.5774				
25	160	0.3420	-0.9397	-0.3640				
26	170	0.1736	-0.9848	-0.1763				
27	180	0.0000	-1.0000	0.0000				
28	190	-0.1736	-0.9848	0.1763				
29	200	-0.3420	-0.9397	0.3640				
30	210	-0.5000	-0.8660	0.5774				
31	220	-0.6428	-0.7660	0.8391				
32	230	-0.7660	-0.6428	1.1918				
33	240	-0.8660	-0.5000	1.7321				
34	250	-0.9397	-0.3420	2.7475				
35	260	-0.9848	-0.1736	5.6713				
36	270	-1.0000	0.0000					
37	280	-0.9848	0.1736	-5.6713				
38	290	-0.9397	0.3420	-2.7475				
39	300	-0.8660	0.5000	-1.7321				
40	310	-0.7660	0.6428	-1.1918				
41	320	-0.6428	0.7660	-0.8391				
42	330	-0.5000	0.8660	-0.5774				
43	340	-0.3420	0.9397	-0.3640				
44	350	-0.1736	0.9848	-0.1763				
45	360	0.0000	1.0000	0.0000				

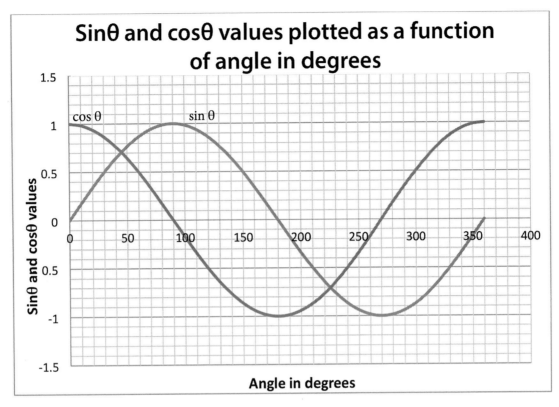

Sinθ and cosθ values plotted as a function of angle in degrees

Angle in degrees

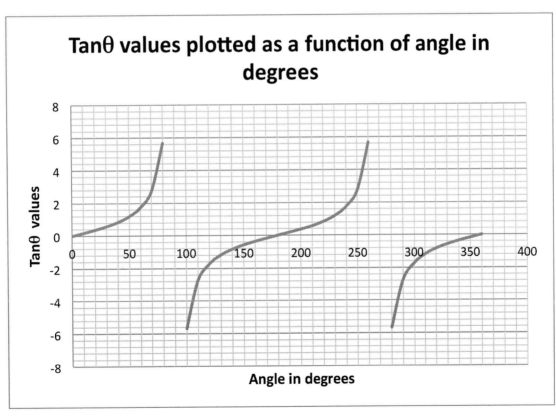

Tanθ values plotted as a function of angle in degrees

Angle in degrees

EXAMPLE 3

Plot the function y(t) = 100t - 4.9t² in the range t = 0 to 20 s

Solution:

In this problem, the increment in time Δ*t* is not given. We will choose a convenient time interval, say 0.5 s. We will enter the data on time t and y(t) calculated as a function of time in two columns. You may choose any columns you like and you may begin from any row. Usually you will use the first few rows for explanations. This information will be helpful for solving the problem and for the future use.

- In the Excel worksheet, we have used cells A6 and B6 as labels.

- Data entered in the cell A7 is 0

- You wish to increment the time intervals by 0.5 s. You will give this data as an absolute variable. We have entered the value 0.5 in the cell B3. Since this value will be used for the calculations, you will not give any other information in this cell. Information about the units etc. were given in the cells A3 and C3.

- In the cell A8 you enter =A7+$B$3 and press enter on the keyboard. The $ signs indicate that this is an absolute variable with respect to both column and row.

- Highlight the cells A8 thro ugh A47, Fill Down. You would notice that the time is incremented in increments of 0.5 s and entered in the proper cells.

- In the cell B7, you enter =100*A7-(4.9*(A7^2)) and press enter on the keyboard. The calculated value will be displayed in the cell.

- You highlight the cells B7 through B47 and Fill Down. You notice that the values of y(t) are calculated and entered in the appropriate cells.

- To plot the data, highlight the cells A6 through A47, and B6 through B47. Click on the graphics button, select x-y scatter plot, click on a smooth curve with data points and finish the plot. Add the appropriate la be l s and title as detailed in the text.

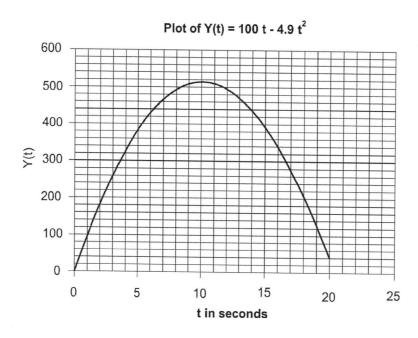

EXAMPLE 3

	A	B	C	D	E	F
1	**Example 3 Plot of y(t) = 100t - 4.9 t^2**					
2	Plot the equation y(t) = 100t - 4.9t^2, in the range t =0 to t = 20 s					
3	Δt=	0.5	s			
4	Equation entered in cell A8 = A7+$B$3					
5	Equation entered in cell B7 = 100*A7-(4.9*(A7^2))					
6	t(s)	Y(t)				
7	0	0				
8	0.5	48.775				
9	1	95.1				
10	1.5	138.975				
11	2	180.4				
12	2.5	219.375				
13	3	255.9				
14	3.5	289.975				
15	4	321.6				
16	4.5	350.775				
17	5	377.5				
18	5.5	401.775				
19	6	423.6				
20	6.5	442.975				
21	7	459.9				
22	7.5	474.375				
23	8	486.4				
24	8.5	495.975				
25	9	503.1				
26	9.5	507.775				
27	10	510				
28	10.5	509.775				
29	11	507.1				
30	11.5	501.975				
31	12	494.4				
32	12.5	484.375				
33	13	471.9				
34	13.5	456.975				
35	14	439.6				
36	14.5	419.775				
37	15	397.5				
38	15.5	372.775				
39	16	345.6				
40	16.5	315.975				
41	17	283.9				
42	17.5	249.375				
43	18	212.4				
44	18.5	172.975				
45	19	131.1				
46	19.5	86.775				
47	20	40				

EXAMPLE 4

During the free fall of an object, the distance traveled as a function of time was recorded. The experimental data are given below:

Time(s)	Distance (m)
0	0
0.054	0.05
0.09	0.1
0.12	0.15
0.145	0.2
0.168	0.25
0.189	0.3
0.208	0.35

Plot the distance traveled (y-axis) vs. time (x-axis). Fit the data to a polynomial of order 2, $y = c_1 + c_2t + c_3t^2$. Give the best fitted equation and comment on the physical significance of the coefficients c_1, c_2 and c_3.

Solution:

Enter the data in two columns in an Excel worksheet. Select and highlight the data you wish to plot. Click on Insert on the Main menu. This opens a new Title bar. Click on the Scatter. You have the options: Scatter with only Markers, Scatter with Markers and smooth lines, Scatter with smooth lines, Scatter with straight lines and Markers, Scatter with straight liines. Choose Scatter with only Markers. A chart will pop up on the work sheet. Right click on the chart, chart tools will show up on the Ribbons and a new dialog box. Click on Add Trend Line. A new Dialog box Trend line options come up. If you are not sure of which of the equation you should use, you can try them and see which one gives you the best fit. In this case, choose a polynomial fit of order 2. Go to Options, set the intercepts as appropriate. If you do not know exactly what the intercept is, leave it blank, the fit program will give you the best fitted value. Click on the box to Display equation on the chart and click on the box to display R-squared value on the chart, and click OK. The graph looks like as follows:

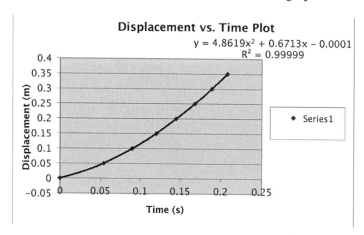

You find an expression similar to the following on the chart

$$y = 4.8619x^2 + 0.6713\ x - 0.0001$$

$$R^2 = 1$$

Some of you who studied physics mechanics before know that if you drop a ball vertically downwards with an initial velocity v_0 downwards, the displacement of the body as a function of time (t) may be written as $y = (1/2)\ gt^2 + v_0 t + y_0$. Here, you are measuring the displacement y as positive downwards. v_0 (m/s) is the initial velocity, y_0 (m) is the initial value of y at $t = 0$, and $(1/2)\ g = 4.9$ m/s^2. The value you got 4.8619 is to be rounded off to the significant digit 4.9 which is close to the expected value of 4.9 m/s^2

VI. Home Assignment Problems

1. Draw a graph of the function
    $y(x) = 2x^4 - x^3 + 8$
    In the range x = -3 to x = +5 at intervals of $\Delta x = 0.2$

2. Draw a graph of the function
    $y(t) = 200\ t - 4.9\ t^2$
    In the range $t = 0$ to $t = 40\ s$ at intervals of $\Delta t = 0.5\ s$

    What type of curve did you get?

3. Plot the function
    $y(t) = 100 - 9.8t$
    in the range $t = 0$ to $t = 20$ s

    What type of curve did you get? What is the slope of the curve?

4. Plot the function
    $$y\ (x) = \left(\frac{1}{6}\right)^x$$

    In the range x = 0.1 to x = 2

5. Plot the function
    $y = 45/x$ for values of x in the range x = 1 to x = 90

6. During the free fall of an object, the distance traveled as a function of time was measured. The experimental data are given below:

Time(s)	Distance Traveled (m)
0	0.0
0.5	3.7
1	9.9
1.5	18.5
2	29.6
2.5	43.1
3	59.1
3.5	77.5
4	98.4
4.5	121.7
5	147.5
5.5	175.7
6	206.4
6.5	239.5
7	275.1
7.5	313.1
8	353.6
8.5	396.5

Plot the graph distance traveled (y - axis) versus time (x - axis). Fit the data to a polynomial

$$y = c_1 + c_2 t + c_3 t^2$$

Find the best fitted values of c_1, c_2, and c_3 and comment on the physical significance of these quantities.

First plot the data points only. Then right click on any data point. A pop menu shows up. Click on **Add Trend Line**, another pop up menu shows up, choose the appropriate functional relationship between the quantities plotted and click on **Display Equation** on chart and **R-squared** value on chart.

7. In a free fall of an object, the velocity as a function of time was measured. The experimental data are given below:

Time(s)	Velocity (m/s)
0.0	0.0
0.5	4.905
1	9.81
1.5	14.715
2	19.62
2.5	24.525
3	29.43
3.5	34.335
4	39.24
4.5	44.145
5	49.05
5.5	53.955
6	58.86
6.5	63.765
7	68.67
7.5	73.575
8	78.48
8.5	83.385
9	88.29
9.5	93.195
10	98.1

Plot the graph velocity (y-axis) versus time (x-axis). Fit the data to a linear equation of the type

$$y = mx + c$$

Find the best fitted values of m and c and comment on the physical significance of these quantities.

First plot the data points only. Then right click on any data point. A pop menu shows up. Click on **Add Trend Line**, another pop up menu shows up, choose the appropriate functional relationship between the quantities plotted and click on **Display Equation** on chart and **R-squared** value on chart.

I. Introduction and Objectives

In this laboratory class, you will be introduced to the vernier caliper and the micrometer caliper, which are used to measure the lengths of small objects to a better precision than the rulers and meter sticks you are familiar with. Employing these instruments, you will be measuring the dimensions of some objects and determining their volumes. By measuring their masses using a laboratory balance, you will calculate the densities of the materials of the objects. Using a micrometer caliper, you will estimate the number of pages in a book.

II. Equipment

Vernier caliper, micrometer caliper, a cylinder, a sphere, a wooden block and any textbook

III. Theory

The least count of an instrument is the smallest subdivision that can be measured without estimating. The least count of a meter stick or a ruler calibrated in cm and graduated to mm is 1 mm or 0.1 cm. Using a vernier caliper or a micrometer caliper; you will be able to measure the length to a much higher precision.

When you use a meter stick to measure the length of an object, you must have noticed that the length of the object is not always an integral multiple of one mm. You can estimate the fractional part but the estimated value is subjective and uncertain. The vernier caliper and the micrometer caliper are used to measure the fractional part with high precision.

Vernier Caliper

The vernier caliper consists of a main scale and a movable jaw with a vernier scale. The span of the lower jaw is useful for measuring the linear dimensions of objects. The span of the upper jaw is employed to measure the inner diameter of a cylinder, the distance between surfaces etc.

The main scale is calibrated in cm and graduated in mm. A measurement is made by closing the jaws on the object. The length of the object is given by the point where the '0' of the vernier scale coincides with the main scale. The length of the object is measured by reading the main scale and the fractional part employing the vernier scale. The main scale and the vernier scale readings are added to obtain the measurement of an object. Most of the vernier calipers available in the market fall in one of the following two categories:

1. The main scale is calibrated in cm and graduated in mm (0.1 cm or 1/10 cm). The vernier scale has 10 divisions such that each division is of 9/10 (0.9) as long as the main scale division. Hence, 10 divisions on the vernier scale are of the same length as '9'divisions on the main scale. Thus, each division on the vernier scale offsets 1/10 of the main scale division. The least count of the vernier is 1/10 of the main scale division and is equal to 0.1 mm or 0.01 cm.

2. The main scale is calibrated in cm and graduated in mm. The vernier scale has 20 divisions. Here, 20 divisions on the vernier scale offset 1 mm on the main scale. For each division of the vernier scale the offset is (1/20) of 1 mm = 0.05 mm. Thus, the least count of the vernier is 0.05 mm.

In general, n divisions on the vernier scale offsets one division on the main scale, and the least count of the vernier is (1/ n) of the main scale division.

The main scale gives a measurement to one mm, such as 3.5 cm or 35 mm. If the least count of the vernier is 0 .05 mm and five vernier divisions coincide with the main scale division, the fractional value is equal to 0.05 x 5 = 0.25 mm or 0.025 cm. When we add this fractional value to the main scale reading, we get 3.525 cm or 35.25 mm. You can give the value to one more significant digit to include the estimated value of the fractional part. If the vernier division perfectly matches with the main scale division, you will add a '0' as the least significant digit resulting 3.5250-cm or 35.250-mm. Of particular interest is the situation when a particular vernier division is right to the main scale division and the next vernier division is to the left of the next main scale division. In this case, you may add 5 or any other appropriate digit estimating the fractional part. If you decide to add '5' as the least significant digit, the result will be 3.525**5** cm or 35.25**5** mm. Here, you have measured the value to '4' significant digits and the least significant digit is given in bold face; this is the estimated digit.

Zero Error

Before making a measurement, you should check the zero error of the instrument. With no object placed, you will close the jaws and check if the zero of the main scale coincides with the zero of the vernier scale. If the zero of the vernier scale is right of the zero of the main scale, you will note the vernier scale reading and subtract this reading from all the measurements you make with this instrument. If the vernier zero is to the left of the main scale zero, you will add this reading to all the measurements you make with this instrument to get the true measurements.

Micrometer Caliper

The micrometer caliper is employed to measure, with high precision, the lengths of small objects such as the diameter of a wire, the thickness of a sheet etc. The object to be measured is placed between the parallel-faced jaws. One of the jaws (anvil) is fixed and the other is movable (spindle). The movable jaw can be moved toward or away from the anvil by rotating the thimble. Most of the micrometer calipers are equipped with a ratchet arrangement so that excessive force may not be applied to the spindle during a measurement, which can potentially damage the screw mechanism. The ratchet arrangement allows you to apply a constant force. When the applied force exceeds a certain a value, the screw mechanism slips.

As you rotate the thimble, a high precision screw mechanism moves the spindle. The distance between two consecutive threads of the screw is called the 'pitch' of the screw. For one revolution of the thimble, the spindle moves by a linear distance equal to the pitch of the screw. The thimble moves over the sleeve. The axial line and the graduations on the sleeve serve as the main scale. The main scale is usually graduated in ½ mm (0.5 mm). The pitch of the screw is also ½ mm. Thus, for one complete revolution of the thimble, the spindle moves by a linear distance of ½ mm. Usually, the graduations on the circular scale on the thimble are divided into 50 equal parts. Thus, each division on the thimble corresponds to 1/50th of ½ mm = 1/100 mm = 0.01 mm. The least count of the micrometer caliper is 0.01 mm. The thimble makes two full revolutions for each mm on the main scale.

Since the pitch of the screw is ½ mm, the thimble makes two complete revolutions for one-mm advance of the spindle. One should be careful to note the reading on the ½ mm scale in the lower portion of the main scale. For example, if the axial line on the main scale crosses the circular scale on the thimble say at 35, and if the thimble is making the first rotation, the thimble reading will be 0. 35 mm. Whereas, if the thimble is making the second rotation, the thimble reading will be 0.5 + 0.35 = 0.85 mm, which will be added to the main scale reading.

Hold the object between the anvil and the spindle. Rotate the thimble clockwise until the object is loosely held between the anvil and the spindle. Rotate the ratchet gently clockwise until the screw mechanism slips. The main scale reading is obtained by noting the reading on the main scale and the edge of the thimble. The reading o n t he thimble is obtained by reading the circular scale o n t he thimble and the intersection of the reading line on the main scale. The length of the object is obtained by adding the main scale and the thimble readings.

Zero Error

The zero error of the micrometer caliper is measured by rotating the screw until the jaw is closed with no object inserted. If the zero of the thimble does not coincide with the main scale, you have to correct

the measurements for the zero error. If the zero of the thimble is to the left of the zero of the main scale, you will subtract the thimble reading from all the observations you do with this instrument. If the thimble reading is to the right of the zero of the main scale, you will add the thimble reading to all the measurements you do with this instrument.

Laboratory Balances

Varieties of laboratory balances are employed for the determination of the mass of an object. The commonly used balances are:

1. Chemical balance
2. Beam balance
3. Digital Balance

In a chemical balance, the unknown mass is compared against the weights of a known mass. In beam balances, the weights on the beams balance the unknown mass on the platform. Electronic balances give digital readouts of the mass directly to the significant digit.

Density

The density of an object is defined as mass per unit volume.

> **Density** (ρ) = mass of the object (m) /volume of the object (V)

Measure the mass of the object using any laboratory balance available to you. The volumes of some regular shaped objects can be calculated using the following formulae.

> **Regular objects:** $V = l \times b \times h$ (length x breadth x height) (2.1)

> **Regular cylinder:** $V = \pi r^2 h$ (2.2)
> (Where πr^2 is the cross-sectional area of the base and h is the height)

> **Sphere:** $V = (4/3)\pi r^3$ (2.3)
> (Where r is the radius of the sphere)

Units

The SI unit of density is kg/m^3. Using the vernier caliper or micrometer caliper, you will be measuring the length in cm or mm. Convert them to meters.

If the measured length is in cm, divide the quantity by 100 to get the length in meters. If the measured length is in mm, divide the value by 1000 to get the value in meters. If you have measured the mass in grams, divide the value by 1000 to get the mass in kg.

If you have calculated the volume in cubic cm (cc), divide the volume in cc by one million (10^6) to get the volume in cubic meters. You may also express the density in CGS units (g/cm^3). However, we will use SI units for all the measurements in this laboratory.

Table 2.1: Densities of some materials

Material	Density (kg/m³)
Hydrogen (0°C, 1 atm)	0.090
Helium (0°C, 1 atm)	0.178
Oxygen	1.43
Air (30°C)	1. 16
Pine wood	$0.4\text{-}0.6 \times 10^3$
Wood (general)	$(0.3 - 0.9) \times 10^3$
Cork	$(0.2 - 0.3) \times 10^3$
Ice	0.92×10^3
Water (20°C)	1×10^3
Aluminum	2.7×10^3
Iron	7.9×10^3
Nickel	8.8×10^3
Copper	8.9×10^3
Silver	10.5×10^3
Lead	11.3×10^3
Mercury	13.6×10^3
Gold	19.3×10^3
Uranium nucleus	3×10^{17}
Neutron star	$\sim 10^{18}$
Black hole	$\sim 10^{19}$

Data Collection and Analysis

PART I - MEASUREMENT OF THE DENSITY OF THE MATERIAL OF A CYLINDER

You will measure the length and diameter of the cylinder using the vernier caliper. The radius is obtained by dividing the diameter by 2. Find the volume using Eq. (2.2). Measure the mass, m of the cylinder using a balance.

Least count of the vernier caliper =

Zero error of the vernier caliper =

Table 2.2: Measurement of the density of a cylindrical object

Reading #	Length of the cylinder h (cm)	Length of the cylinder h (m)	Diameter of the cylinder d (cm)	Radius of the cylinder r (m)	Volume of the cylinder $V = \pi r^2 h$ (m³)	Mass of the cylinder m (kg)	Density $\rho = m/V$ (kg/m³)
1							
2							
3							
4							
Average							

Measured (average) value of the density of _____ =

Accepted/True value (from *Table 2.1*) =

$$\text{Percent accuracy} = \left| \frac{\text{Measured value - Accepted value}}{\text{Accepted value}} \right| \times 100$$

PART II - MEASUREMENT OF THE DENSITY OF THE MATERIAL OF A SPHERE

Using a vernier caliper, measure the diameter of the sphere. The radius of the sphere is obtained by dividing the diameter by 2. Calculate the volume o f the sphere using Eq. (2.3). Measure the mass of the sphere using a balance and obtain its mass, m. Calculate the density of the material.

Table 2.3: Measurement of the density of the material of a sphere

Reading #	Diameter of the sphere (cm)	Radius of the sphere (m)	Volume of the sphere $V = (4/3) \pi r^3$ (m³)	Mass of the sphere m (kg)	Density $\rho = m /V$ (kg/m³)
1					
2					
3					
4					
Average					

Measured (average) value of the density of _____ =

Accepted/True value (from *Table 2.1*) =

Percent accuracy = $\left| \dfrac{\text{Measured value - Accepted value}}{\text{Accepted value}} \right|$ x 100

PART III - MEASUREMENT OF THE DENSITY OF THE MATERIAL OF A BLOCK

Measure the length, breadth and the depth of the block using the vernier caliper. Calculate the volume of the block using (Eq. 2.1). Weigh the block and obtain its mass, *m*. Knowing the volume and the mass of the block, calculate the density of the material of the block.

Table 2.4: Measurement of the density of the material of a block

Reading #	Length l (cm)	Length l (m)	Breadth b (cm)	Breadth b (m)	Height h (cm)	Height h (m)	Volume $V = l \times b \times h$ m^3	Mass m (kg)	Density $\rho = m/V$ (kg/m³)
1									
2									
3									
4									
Average									

Measured (average) value of the density of _____ =

Accepted/True value (from *Table 2.1*) =

Percent accuracy = $\left| \dfrac{\text{Measured value - Accepted value}}{\text{Accepted value}} \right|$ x 100

PART IV - ESTIMATION OF THE NUMBER OF PAGES IN A BOOK USING A MICROMETER CALIPER

Measure the thickness of a sheet of a book and the total thickness of the book (excluding the covers) using a micrometer caliper. If you divide the thickness of the book by the thickness of a sheet, you will get the number of sheets in the book. Compare the measured value with the number of sheets in the book.

Table 2.5: Estimation of the number of sheets in a book using micrometer caliper

Reading #	Thickness of one sheet of a book t (mm)	Thickness of one sheet of a book t (m)	Thickness of the book excluding covers T (cm)	Thickness of the book excluding covers T (m)	Measured # of sheets in the book T/t
1					
2					
3					
4					
Average					

Actual number of sheets in the book = Number of pages in the book/2

Measured number of sheets in the book =

$$\text{Percent accuracy} = \left| \frac{\text{Measured number of sheets - Actual number of sheets}}{\text{Actual number of sheets}} \right| \times 100$$

Note 1: You enter all the data directly in an Excel worksheet and do all the calculations using the Excel program.

Note 2: You present the density measurements in SI units, i.e. in kg/m^3.

IV. Home Assignment

(Give answers to the following questions in your laboratory report)

1. You were given a circular sheet of aluminum of radius 10 cm and thickness 0.25 mm, find the mass of the sheet. Use the value for the density of aluminum given in *Table 2.1*.

2. Give a list of sources of error in the density measurements. Identify systematic and random errors in your measurements. How do you minimize them?

3. For measuring the number of pages in a book using the micrometer screw, would you prefer a textbook with a mixture of art paper and ordinary paper or sheets of only one kind? Give your reasons.

4. In Part I, you measured the density of the material of the cylinder. You employed the vernier caliper to measure the diameter d, and the height h, of the cylinder. Let the least count of the vernier caliper is the uncertainty in the measurements of the diameter and the height. From the uncertainties in the diameter and the height, calculate the uncertainty ΔV (see Example 1 and section 2.3 Propagation of errors in Chapter 1 under General Laboratory Information) in the volume V. If the mass is measured to a high precision (the uncertainty ~ 0), calculate the uncertainty in the measured value of the density. What is the accuracy of your measurement?

Uniformly Accelerated Motion in One Dimension

Experiments 3 & 4

I.   Introduction and Objectives

In this chapter, you will be investigating the kinematics of an object moving with constant acceleration. A popular example of this motion is an object moving freely under the action of the gravitational force due to the Earth. All objects moving in the Earth's gravitational field experience a constant acceleration of 9.81 m/s² directed towards the center of the Earth. This value is usually taken as constant, though the acceleration due to gravity varies slightly at different geographic locations on the surface of the Earth; for example, it decreases as you go to high altitudes or into deep mines. Here, we neglect the effects due to air resistance, which are small for dense objects.

II.   Theory

Consider an object moving in a straight line along the x-axis with a constant acceleration, a. Let its initial position be x_{init} and its initial velocity be v_{init} at $t = 0$. The kinematics of motion can be expressed by the following equations

$$x(t) = x_{init} + v_{init}\, t + \frac{1}{2}at^2 \tag{3.1}$$

$$v(t) = v_{init} + at \tag{3.2}$$

$$v(t) = v_{init} + 2ax \tag{3.3}$$

$$x_t = v_{avg}\, t \tag{3.4}$$

$$v_{avg\,=} \frac{(v_{init} + v_{final})}{2} \tag{3.5}$$

Where $x(t)$, read as "x as a function of time t" (is not equivalent to x times t), gives the values of the displacement x for different values of t. Similarly, $v(t)$, read as "v as a function of time t" gives the velocity as a function of the elapsed time t. $v(x)$, read as "velocity as a function of x" gives the value of the velocity for a specific value of x. One can calculate the velocity, $v(x)$, for different values of x. Here, x is the displacement, v_{init} is the initial velocity, v_{final} is the final velocity, t is the time elapsed and v_{avg} is the average velocity.

If you drop, say, a tennis ball (initial velocity zero) from the top floor of a building, the displacement and velocity as a function of time may be written as

$$y - y_0 = -\frac{1}{2}gt^2 \qquad or \qquad y = y_0 - \frac{1}{2}gt^2 \tag{3.6}$$

$$-v(t) + v_{init} = -gt \qquad or \qquad v(t) = +gt \qquad (v_{init} = 0) \tag{3.7}$$

Here, we have chosen a coordinate system where the positive y-direction is upwards. Both y and y_0 give the coordinates as measured from the ground level. In this coordinate system, the acceleration due to gravity g is directed downwards and is negative. The velocity is also directed downwards, therefore it is negative as well. In experiment 3, you will be measuring the displacement y, the velocity v, and the acceleration a as functions of time using a picket fence in free fall, and you will then calculate the value of g. In experiment 4, you will be measuring the displacement y as a function of time for a tossed ball using a motion detector and calculate the value of g.

I. Objectives

Measure the acceleration due to gravity (g) with high precision employing a picket fence and a photo-gate.

II. Equipment

Picket Fence, Windows PC/Mac, Photo-gate, Universal Lab Interface, Logger Pro Software, Excel Software

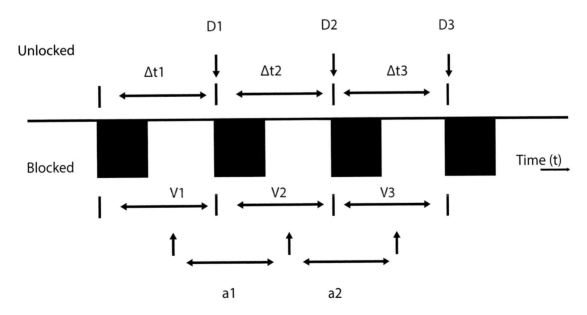

Figure 3.1: Picket-fence timing

III. Theory

You will use a 'picket fence' (a rectangular piece of plastic with alternate opaque and transparent sections) for the measurements. The program is set up to analyze the motion of the picket fence as it moves through the photo-gate. As the picket fence falls through the gate, the time taken by the picket fence to cover the distance between opaque bands is measured. A built-in timing routine measures times to a precision of better than $1\,\mu s$ (10^{-6} s).

As the picket fence passes through the photo-gate, the light from the LED (light emitting diode) is blocked by the opaque regions of the picket fence. Fig. 3.1 shows the light intensity at the photo-detector as a function of time. In this experiment you will be measuring the time intervals (Δt_1, Δt_2, Δt_3...) as leading opaque edges of the picket fence pass through the photo-gate beam. These time intervals are displayed in a data table. If you enter the distance between the leading edges of the opaque bands in the length of the object field, the program calculates the displacement, velocity and acceleration as functions of time. However, you will find it illustrative to do the calculations yourself using the Excel software.

CALCULATING THE VELOCITY AS A FUNCTION OF TIME

The distance traveled is $D1$ in a time interval of Δt_1. The average velocity in the time interval Δt_1 is

$$v_1 = D_1/\Delta t_1 = \text{Distance traveled } (D_1) \,/\, \text{Time elapsed } (\Delta t_1)$$

The average velocity corresponds to the instantaneous velocity at the middle of the time interval ($\Delta t_1/2$).

CALCULATION OF THE DISPLACEMENT AS A FUNCTION OF TIME

The distance between two opaque bands is constant. For the picket fence provided it is equal to 0.05 m. The displacements are obtained by multiplying the distance between opaque bands and the number of such bands crossing the photo-gate. The elapsed times are obtained by adding the corresponding time intervals ($\Sigma\Delta t$).

If the distance between two opaque bands is D and if n bands have crossed the photo-gate, the displacement

$$d = nD$$

which corresponds to time $\Sigma\Delta t_n$. Using these data, one can plot a displacement vs. time graph.

CALCULATION OF ACCELERATION AS A FUNCTION OF TIME

The acceleration $a = \Delta v/\Delta t =$ (change in the velocity)/elapsed time (time between midpoints of the velocity intervals). The accelerations are assumed to have occurred at a time halfway between the midpoints of the velocity intervals.

Note that the times and the time intervals for the displacements, velocities and the accelerations are all different. As the picket fence is released, it picks up higher speeds with time, and the time intervals to cover the same length of the picket fence decreases. Therefore, the time intervals Δt_1, Δt_2, Δt_3, ...Δtn will be different and decrease with time.

v_1 corresponds to time $\Delta t_1 / 2$

v_2 corresponds to time $\Delta t_1 + \Delta t_2 / 2$

v_3 corresponds to time $\Delta t_1 + \Delta t_2 + \Delta t / 2$

v_n corresponds to time $\Sigma \Delta t_{n-1} + \Delta t_n / 2$

a_1 corresponds to $(\Delta t_1 / 2) + (\Delta t_2 / 2)$

a_2 corresponds to $\Delta t_1 + (\Delta t_2 / 2) + (\Delta t_3 / 2)$

a_n corresponds to $\Sigma \Delta t_{n-1} + (\Delta t_n / 2) + (\Delta t_{n+1} / 2)$

IV. Experimental Details

First, test if the photo-gate is working or not by blocking the beam using your hand. It is working when the red light on the photo-gate glows when the beam is intercepted and the red LED is off when the beam is not intercepted.

Open the Logger Pro Software (c-drive, Program Files, Vernier Software, Logger Pro)

Open Motion Detector Software (Experiments, Motion Detector, Motion Detector)

You will open a worksheet that contains the menu bar, a toolbar containing a collect button, graph and data windows, and a status bar.

Experiment:	Sampling; Photo-gate timing
Setup:	Sensors, UL1, DG1, Photo-gate, Photo-gate
Setup:	<u>Mode</u>: Data collection, Photo-gate timing, <u>Sampling</u>: Vernier Picket Fence
Graph Options:	Graph Features, Axis Options

Here you can control what is plotted on the two axes as well as the scale used. If the data are varying smoothly you may use the auto mode to plot the data. However if you have large fluctuations such as spikes in the data you would be better off plotting the data in the manual mode. When you plot the data in the manual mode, you will be able to choose an appropriate scale so that you can visually inspect the data and discard the visibly erroneous data such as a spike in the beginning, which may be due to electronics.

Graph Layout: Graph layout allows you to control the way multiple graph panes are shown in the graph window. Choose the desired option and click OK.

Sensors: Click on DG1 and OK.

Sampling: Select Vernier Picket Fence and click OK.

Window Menu: <u>New Tall Window</u>: New tall window creates a new window. The current window is halved in width and the new window is created beside the resized active window.

New window has the following choices:

Graph: Choose Graph to create a data plot

Table: Choose Table to create a new data table.

V. Data Collection

Click on the Experiment to open the pull down menu. Click on Collect and release the picket fence. Make sure that the picket fence does not hit the ground, in which case it may break. When the picket fence has passed through the photo-gate click on the **Stop** button. Now you should see data in 5 columns. Make the following graphs:

1. Displacement vs. Time

2. Velocity vs. Time

3. Acceleration vs. Time

For each of the graphs, choose an appropriate scale manually or use Auto mode. The graph should cover most of the page.

Using PASCO Capstone/Datastudio Software

SET-UP

Open *DataStudio*, click on *create experiment* option. Plug the yellow wire of the motion sensor into digital channel 1, and the black wire into digital channel 2. Click *setup* button on the top left corner. Click *choose interface* button. Select *Science Workshop* 500 interface. An image will now appear in the window. Select the left most yellow highlighted port (digital channel 1). Now select the "motion sensor" sensor option. Select the "motion sensor" tab option. Set the Standard Distance to 1m. Now close the experiment setup window. Now on the top left hand corner under "data" you should have position, velocity, and acceleration folders. When you are ready to start data collection hit the "start" button.

DATA ANALYSIS

In order to graph position, velocity, or acceleration you need to select the graph option under the displays menu of the bottom left hand corner. Select the run and parameter you want to graph and hit ok. Then fit the graph with the appropriate functional relationship.

VI. Data Analysis and Calculations

FITTING PROCEDURE

Choose a range on the graph you wish to fit the data to an equation. Fit each of the graphs with the following equations:

1. $y = Ax$ (Proportional)
2. $y = A + Bx$ (Linear)
3. $y = A + Bx + Cx^2$ (Quadratic)

Make sure that the fitted equation and R^2 values appear on the plots for each of the plots. Note that R^2 value close to 1 corresponds to the best fitted values. The deviation of R^2 value from 1 is an indication of a bad fit.

VII. Questions

1. Which of the three equations listed above gave you best fits for following graphs?
    - displacement *vs.* time
    - velocity *vs.* time
    - acceleration *vs.* time

    For each of the best fit you obtained, comment on why that particular equation gave you the best fit and not the other two equations.

2. How do you obtain the value of the acceleration due to gravity from each of the following plots using the computer fits?
    - displacement *vs.* time
    - velocity *vs.* time
    - acceleration *vs.* time

3. If you measure the area under the acceleration vs. time graph in the time range 0 to t, what physical quantity do you get? And the value obtained corresponds to what time?

4. If you measure the area under the velocity vs. time graph in the time range 0 to t, what physical quantity do you get? And the value obtained corresponds to what time?

5. At any point on the displacement vs. time graph, what does the slope of the tangent correspond?

6. At any point on the velocity vs. time graph, what does the slope of the tangent correspond?

7. If you fit the velocity (*y*-axis) vs. time (*x*- axis) data to a straight line of the type $y = mx + c$, what is the physical significance of the slope (*m*) and the *y*-intercept *c* when $x = 0$?

8. If you fit the distance (y-axis) vs. time (x-axis) data to a quadratic equation of the type $y = A + Bx + Cx^2$, what are the physical significances of the constants A, B and C?

9. If you release the picket fence from different heights from the photo-gate, would that affect the value of the acceleration due to gravity 'g' obtained? Explain.

10. You fitted the displacement vs. time data to a quadratic equation of the type $y = A + Bx + Cx^2$ where y is the displacement and x is the time. If you release the picket fence from a different height, would the constants A, B, and C be different? Explain.

Your lab report will have the printouts of the data, fitted plots and answers to the above questions and (or) your comments.

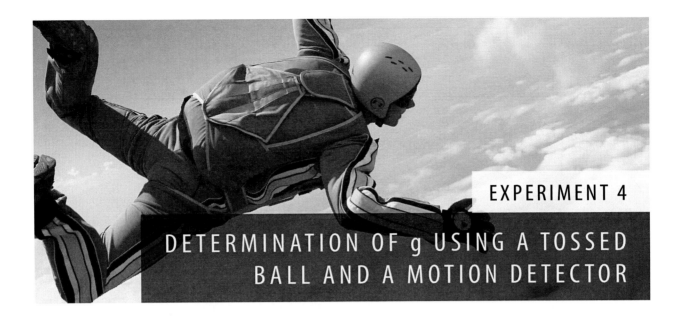

DETERMINATION OF g USING A TOSSED BALL AND A MOTION DETECTOR

I. Introduction and Objectives

All the objects near the Earth experience a gravitational force directed towards the center of the Earth. Because of the gravitational force, the objects will experience acceleration due to gravity. The acceleration due to gravity is always directed towards the center of the Earth irrespective of the object moving upwards, downwards or sideways. If you toss a ball upward with an initial velocity, the magnitude of the velocity of the ball decreases because of the acceleration due to gravity. In this experiment, by measuring the displacement of a ball thrown upwards as a function of time, you will calculate the acceleration due to gravity. You will use a motion detector to measure the displacement as a function of time.

OBJECTIVE

To determine the acceleration due to gravity 'g' using a tossed ball and a motion detector

II. Equipment

PC or Power Mac, Motion detector, Universal lab Interface, basketball, wire mesh protector for the motion detector.

III. Theory

If you toss a ball vertically upwards with an initial velocity say v_{init}, the displacement $y(t)$, y as a function of time (t) may be written in the form

$$y(t) = y_0 + v_{init}\, t - \tfrac{1}{2}gt^2$$

This is an equation of a parabola. In this experiment, you will toss a ball vertically upwards and measure the displacement as a function of time using a motion detector. From the displacement versus time data, you can obtain the velocity vs. time and the acceleration vs. time data. By fitting the data to the expected relationships as given by the kinematics of motion, you will obtain the value of the acceleration due to gravity.

Using PASCO Capstone/Datastudio Software

SET-UP

Open *DataStudio*, click on *create experiment* option. Plug the yellow wire of the motion sensor into digital channel 1, and the black wire into digital channel 2. Click *setup* button on the top left corner. Click *choose interface* button. Select *Science Workshop* 500 interface. An image will now appear in the window. Select the left most yellow highlighted port (digital channel 1). Now select the "Photo-gate and Picket Fence" sensor option. Select the "Constants" tab and set your band spacing. Now close the experiment setup window. Now on the top left hand corner under "data" you should have position, velocity, and acceleration folders. You launch the basketball vertically upwards. When you are ready to start data collection hit the "start" button. After you are done collecting data, hit the "stop" button.

DATA ANALYSIS

Now that you have completed data acquisition for all your runs it is time to graph the data for each run. Under "displays" select the "graph" option. Now choose a data source by selecting which run and which measurement (position, velocity, and acceleration) you want to graph. We will start with run 1. Select run 1 under the position folder and hit ok. A graph will appear. Next select the "fit" drop down menu and select a quadratic fit. You should get a line through your data points along with a box giving data for your fit. To make another graph select the graph option from the displays menu and select run 1 under the velocity folder and hit ok. Select the "fit" drop down menu and select a linear fit. You should get a line through all your data points along with a box giving data for you fit. To make another graph select the graph option from the displays menu and select run 1 under the acceleration folder and hit ok. Select the "fit" drop down menu and select a linear fit. You should get a line through all your data points along with a box giving data for you fit. Repeat instructions for each run.

IV. Experimental Details

You will choose volleyball or a basketball for this experiment. Larger balls are appropriate because they reflect the ultrasound waves better. Since larger balls experience considerable force of buoyancy, you may get slightly lower value for the acceleration due to gravity. Keep the motion detector on the floor and connect it to the interface and the computer. Start collecting data. Hold the ball on the sides with the fingers of both your hands about 40 cm away from the motion detector. After about one second, toss the ball upwards such that it reaches a height of about 1-2 meters. Catch the ball on its return path when it is approximately 40 cm from the motion detector. Collect the data for a couple of seconds. You will get the plots displacement vs. time, velocity vs. time and acceleration vs. time.

Although you have collected the data for 2-3 seconds, the data of your interest covers only a fraction of a second. You are interested in the data from the instant you have thrown the ball to the instant just before you caught the ball. By carefully inspecting the data, try to identify that region. On the displacement vs. time plot, you would notice a small hump because for a ball thrown vertically upwards, the displacement vs. time plot will be a parabola (Eq: 3.8). Try to identify the small hump that corresponds to a parabola. Mark this region using the markers and you will use only the marked portion of the data for all the calculations and the fits.

If you carefully examine the velocity vs. time plot, you will notice that the velocity increases quite rapidly when you tossed the ball, reaching a maximum value as you leave the ball. Then the velocity decreases linearly because the acceleration due to gravity is acting downwards reaching zero value at its maximum height. As the ball reverses its direction of motion downwards, its velocity is directed downwards and its magnitude increases gradually because of the acceleration due to gravity acting downwards. When you catch the ball, the ball experiences large deceleration for a short time and will be brought to rest (zero velocity) in a short time interval. The region of interest is from the instant after you threw the ball to the instant just before you caught the ball. In the velocity vs. time curve, this region corresponds to a straight line beginning from a certain initial velocity $(+v)$, linearly decreasing to zero and attaining an approximately similar negative $(-v)$ value.

The acceleration due to gravity is constant and is acting all the time in the downward direction irrespective of the ball moving upwards or downwards. If the upward direction is taken as positive, this corresponds to a horizontal line with an approximate value of -9.8 m/s^2 in the acceleration vs. time graph. You can obtain the acceleration due to gravity directly by reading the values at different points on the graph and taking the mean value.

V.   Data Analysis and Calculations

You will obtain the acceleration due to gravity from the displacement vs. time, velocity vs. time and acceleration vs. time graphs.

DISPLACEMENT VS. TIME CURVE

Carefully choose the range on the graph that corresponds to the motion of the ball from the instant you threw the ball to the instant just before you caught the ball. You should be extremely careful in identifying the correct region. If you do not identify the correct region, you are likely to get absurd value for the acceleration due to gravity. Fit the displacement vs. time data in the selected region to a quadratic equation of the type

$$y = A + Bx + Cx^2 \hspace{3cm} (3.8)$$

This equation is of the form

$$y(t) = y_0 + v_0 t + Ct^2$$

y_0 gives the initial value of y when $t = 0$, v_0 is the initial velocity when $t = 0$. The constant C corresponds to $(g/2)$. From the best value of C obtained from the fit program, calculate the value of the acceleration due to gravity g.

VELOCITY VS. TIME CURVE

Identify the region on the velocity vs. time graph that corresponds to the motion of the ball from the instant you threw the ball to the instant just before you caught the ball. Fit only the selected region to a linear equation

$$y = A + Bx \qquad\qquad (3.9)$$

This equation is of the form

$$v = v_0 + gt$$

Where v_0 is the initial velocity when $t = 0$.

The best value of B obtained from the fit procedure corresponds to the acceleration due to gravity.

ACCELERATION VS. TIME GRAPH

Identify the correct region as mentioned above and measure the values of the acceleration at different times within the selected region. The average of these values give the acceleration due to gravity 'g'.

VI. Questions

1. The displacement vs. time data were fitted to a quadratic equation in t given by (Eq: 3.8). Interpret the physical significance of the constants A, B, and C.

2. The velocity vs. time data were fitted to linear equation in t given by (Eq: 3.9). Interpret the physical significance of the fitted values A and B.

3. From the best-fitted value of the initial velocity v_0, generate the displacement vs. time and the velocity vs. time plots and compare them with the observed experimental plots.

4. In the acceleration vs. time plot, identify the regions corresponding to:
   - When you were holding the ball
   - when you tossed the ball upwards
   - when the ball was moving upwards and downwards under the acceleration due to gravity, and
   - when you caught the ball during its return path.

   Explain the details.

Vectors

Experiment 5

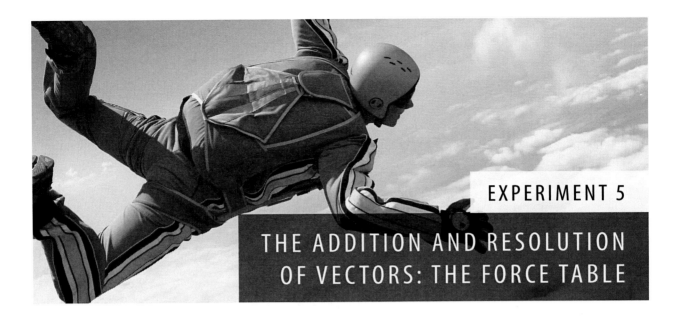

THE ADDITION AND RESOLUTION OF VECTORS: THE FORCE TABLE

I. Introduction and Objectives

Addition and Resolution of Vectors

In this experiment, you will learn about vector quantities and how to manipulate them. Scalar quantities have only magnitude, whereas vector quantities have both magnitude and direction. Examples of scalar quantities are temperature, volume, mass, and money. Examples of vector quantities are displacement, velocity, acceleration, force, and momentum. When we deal with scalar quantities, simple algebraic addition and subtraction methods are applicable. For manipulating the vector quantities, we employ parallelogram law of addition and subtraction.

Both the direction and the magnitude of a vector quantity play important roles in deciding the effect of vector quantities. Let us consider a simple example to show the importance of direction. If you have a small object on a table and if you tie a fine thread and pull it with a constant force in the direction of east, it will be accelerated in that direction. If you apply another force of equal magnitude simultaneously in the direction of west, the object will not move at all. However, if you apply the second force in the direction north, the object will be accelerated in the direction of northeast. Clearly, the direction of a vector quantity also plays a vital role in deciding the effect of the vector quantites.

Let us consider another example. Displacement is a vector quantity. The displacement vector depends on its initial position, final position and the direction of the final position with respect to the initial position. *It does not depend on the path taken.* Suppose you drove 5 km east and then 5 km north, what is your displacement vector? We use Pythagoras Theorem to calculate the magnitude of your displacement from the initial position = $\sqrt{(5^2 + 5^2)}$ = 7.07 km. The magnitude of your displacement vector will be 7.07 km and its direction will be 45° north of east.

In dealing with vector quantities, we realize that both direction and magnitude play important roles. You know how to add, subtract and multiply scalar quantities. Special methods were developed to add, subtract and multiply vector quantities. In this experiment, you will learn how to add and subtract vector quantities.

II.   Equipment

Force table, fine thread, and weights.

III.   Theory

Methods of Vector Addition

Vector quantities are printed in boldface that differentiates them from the scalar quantities. When you write a vector quantity, you may put an arrow on its head to identify it as a vector quantity. Vector manipulation can be done using geometrical or analytical methods. Geometrical methods are somewhat time consuming and are usually employed when the number of vectors involved are a few, whereas analytical methods are more powerful and are commonly employed to solve problems in engineering and science.

Vectors are represented geometrically by means of straight lines with arrows at the tip. The length of the straight line corresponds to the magnitude of the vector drawn to a suitable scale and the arrow gives the direction of the vector. Thus the straight line with an arrow represents both the magnitude and direction of the vector. You may choose any scale convenient to you. For example, 1 cm = 10 N, 1 cm = 20 N, 1 cm = 25 km. We also note that any two-line segments of identical length and direction represent equal vectors. Therefore, parallel vectors of equal magnitude represent identical vectors. Thus a vector can be moved around and equivalently replaced by means of a parallel vector of the same magnitude and direction.

A. GEOMETRICAL METHODS

(a) Parallelogram Method
Resultant of two vectors

Suppose that two or more forces act on an object simultaneously, the net effect produced by all these forces may be represented in magnitude and direction by a single force that is known as the resultant.

To add two vectors **A** and **B** acting on a body in a two dimensional plane, we choose a suitable scale to represent their magnitudes and define their directions with reference to a coordinate system. Then, we draw a parallelogram with **A** and **B** as adjacent sides taking their magnitudes and directions into account. The diagonal of the parallelogram **R**, drawn from the tail of **A** to the tip of **B**, in magnitude and direction represents the sum of the vectors (**A** + **B**). The direction of the resultant may be specified as the angle θ relative to the vector A or relative to the x-axis.

(b) Tip-to -tail Method

To add two vectors **A** and **B** acting on a body in a two dimensional plane employing tip-to-tail method, we choose a suitable scale to represent their magnitudes and define their directions with reference to a coordinate system. Then draw the vectors **A** and **B** such that the tail of the vector **B** coincides with the tip of the vector **A**. The vector drawn from the tail of vector **A** to the tip of vector **B** gives both the magnitude and direction the resultant of the vectors (**A** + **B**). If more than two vectors are to be added, draw the vector **C** such that the tail of the vector **C** coincides with the tip of the vector B. The vector drawn from the tail of **A** to the tip of **C** in magnitude and direction represents the resultant of the vectors (**A** + **B** + **C**). This procedure may be extended to find the resultant of any number of vectors. This is known as the Polygon method and can be employed for the addition and subtraction of vectors in two dimensions. Subtraction of a vector is performed by adding the negative of that vector.

B. ANALYTICAL METHOD

You have seen how to add vector quantities employing geometrical methods. Now, you will be introduced to a powerful method of manipulating the vector quantities known as the analytical method.

Just as you add two or more vector quantities to obtain the resultant, you can resolve any vector quantity into two or more components. For all practical purposes, we can equivalently replace any vector by its components. Of particular interest is resolving a vector into its components along the axes of a rectangular coordinate system. Let **F** be a vector directed at an angle θ with respect to the x-axis. The vector **F** can be replaced by its two components: one of magnitude F cos θ acting along the x-axis and another of magnitude F sin θ acting along the y-axis. One can verify that the vector addition of the components results in the original vector, **F**. Thus if the vector R is the resultant of these components.

$$R^2 = F^2 \sin^2 \theta + F^2 \cos^2 \theta = F^2 (\sin^2 \theta + \cos^2 \theta) = F^2$$

$$\text{And } \tan \theta = R_y / R_x$$

$$\text{Giving, } R = F$$

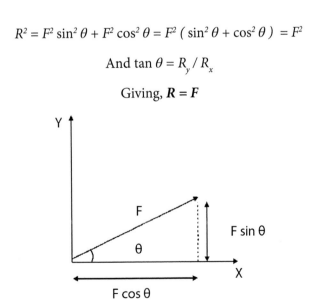

Figure 4.1: Resolving a vector F into two components.

If you have a number of forces acting simultaneously at a point on a body, how do you calculate the resultant of all these forces employing the analytical method?

Let **F**₁, **F**₂, **F**₃ and **F**₄ be the forces acting on the body in a two-dimensional plane. Choose an appropriate Cartesian coordinate system. F_1 may be resolved into its components, F_{1x} along the x-axis and F_{1y} along the y-axis and similarly F_2 may be resolved into its components, F_{2x} along the x-axis and F_{2y} along the y-axis and so on. The x-component of the resultant is obtained by summing the x-components of the vectors to be added and the y-component of the resultant is obtained by summing the y-components of the vectors to be added. As shown in *Fig 4.2*, we will measure all the angles with respect to the positive or negative x-axis. Equivalently you could as well measure all the angles with respect to the positive and the negative y-axis as well.

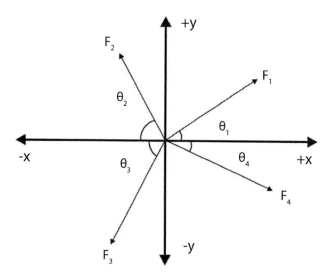

Figure 4.2: Resolving the vectors into their components in a two dimensional plane.

$$F_{1x} = +F_1 \cos \theta_1$$
$$F_{2x} = -F_2 \cos \theta_2$$
$$F_{3x} = -F_3 \cos \theta_3$$
$$F_{4x} = +F_4 \cos \theta_4$$
$$F_{1y} = +F_1 \sin \theta_1$$
$$F_{2y} = +F_2 \sin \theta_2$$
$$F_{3y} = -F_3 \sin \theta_3$$
$$F_{4y} = -F_4 \sin \theta_4$$

$$F_{Rx} = F_{1x} + F_{2x} + F_{3x} + F_{4x} = F_1 \cos \theta_1 - F_2 \cos \theta_2 - F_3 \cos \theta_3 + F_4 \cos \theta_4$$
$$F_{Ry} = F_{1y} + F_{2y} + F_{3y} + F_{4y} = F_1 \sin \theta_1 + F_2 \sin \theta_2 - F_3 \sin \theta_3 - F_4 \sin \theta_4$$
$$|F_R| = \sqrt{F_{Rx}^2 + F_{Ry}^2}$$
$$\tan \phi = \frac{F_{Ry}}{F_{Rx}} \qquad \phi = \tan^{-1}\left(\frac{F_{Ry}}{F_{Rx}}\right)$$

Where |F_R| is the magnitude of the resultant of the vectors **F**₁, **F**₂, **F**₃ and **F**₄, and φ is the angle the resultant makes with respect to the x-axis.

By taking the components of all the vectors along the axes of a fixed coordinate system, you can simply add or subtract the components just as you do in the case of the scalar quantities.

IV. Experimental Details

The force table is a simple apparatus that will enable you to verify the laws of vector addition. The forces are applied to a central ring by means of strings running over pulleys attached to weights. If m is the mass of the hanger and the weights, the force $F = mg$ (m in kg and $g = 9.81$ m/s^2 gives F in Newtons). For this experiment, you may find it convenient to express all the forces in kg. wt. instead of Newtons. If m is the mass of the hanger and the weights, the force $F = m$ kg. wt. You may apply simultaneously a number of forces on the ring such that the ring is in equilibrium, i.e. the net force acting on the ring = zero. This is judged by centering the ring with respect to the central pin. When you apply n forces and obtain the equilibrium condition (the net force acting on the ring = 0), the resultant of any of the $(n - 1)$ forces applied is equal and opposite of the nth force. The nth force is called equilibrant. Thus,

$$\Sigma F = 0; \ F_1 + F_2 + F_3 \ \ldots\ldots\ldots\ldots + F_n = 0$$

OR

$$F_1 + F_2 + F_3 + \ \ldots\ldots\ldots\ldots \ = -F_n$$

Part I. Resultant of Two Equal Forces Applied Perpendicular to Each Other

Apply two forces such that the angle between them is 90° (corresponding to the threads at 30° and 120° or 0° and 90°). Apply equal masses of about 0.2 kg to each hanger. Using a third pulley and weights, find by trial and error the magnitude and direction of the force F_3 (equilibrant) needed to balance the forces F_1 and F_2. Repeat the experiment with the magnitudes of F_1 and F_2 each equal to 0.5 kg. wt. Enter the data in *Table 4.1*.

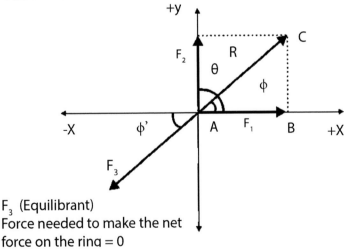

Figure 4.3: Resultant of two equal forces perpendicular to each other.

Note the magnitudes and angular directions of F_1, F_2, and F_3. The angular directions are read on the circular scale of the force table. You may find it convenient to choose the direction of any of the forces to coincide with the zero of the angular scale of the force table.

In *Fig 4.3*, the ring is in equilibrium under the action of three applied forces F_1, F_2 and F_3. That means the net force acting on the ring is equal to zero. If we treat F_3 as the equilibrant, the resultant of $F_1 + F_2$ will be equal and opposite to the equilibrant so that the net force acting on the ring is equal to zero. We will add F_1 and F_2 to get their resultant R and compare whether R is equal in magnitude to F_3 and opposite in direction.

Objective

Find the resultant of the two forces F_1 and F_2 acting at 90° to each other in a plane using (a) the geometrical method and (b) the analytical method and compare the values with the experimentally measured values of the equilibrant.

A. Geometrical Method

In this method, using a protractor and a ruler you will draw the forces to a suitable scale and verify that the resultant of two forces when the body is in equilibrium is equal and opposite to the equilibrant. Choose an appropriate scale, say, 1 cm = 0.05 kg. wt. and draw the lines AB and BC (*Fig 3*) such that they are parallel to the forces and their lengths are proportional to the magnitudes of the forces. Complete the square. The diagonal R in magnitude and direction represents the resultant of these forces.

Suppose that $F_1 = F_2 = 0.2$ kg. wt. and the angle between F_1 and F_2 is equal to 90°. Draw a straight line representing the vector F_1 to a suitable scale. If the scale is 1 kg. wt. = 20 cm, 0.2 kg. wt. corresponds to 4 cm. Therefore, the length of the vector F_1 will be 4 cm. Vector F_2 is perpendicular to vector F_1. Using a protractor, draw F_2 perpendicular to F_1 and the length of F_2 will be 4 cm. You will complete the square and draw the diagonal AC, which represents in magnitude and direction the resultant of F_1 and F_2. If the measured length of R is equal to say 5.6 cm, this corresponds to 0.28 kg. wt. Since the scale is 20 cm = 1 kg. wt., the measured length of 5.6 cm corresponds to 0.28 kg. wt.

The resultant R should be equal in magnitude and opposite in direction to the third force F_3 (equilibrant). You will compare the magnitudes of **R** and F_3 and their directions ϕ and ϕ'. If they are equal within the experimental errors, then the geometrical method of addition of vectors is verified. Enter the data in *Table 4.1*. For details see *Fig 4.3*. The magnitude of the equilibrant force F_3 is entered in the fourth column of *Table 4.1*. The angle ϕ', the force F_3 makes with the negative x-direction is entered in the fifth column of *Table 4.1*. The magnitude of the calculated value of the resultant R is entered in the sixth column of *Table 4.1*. The calculated value of the angle ϕ that R makes with respect to the x-axis is entered in the seventh column of *Table 4.1*. You will compare the calculated values of the resultant R with the measured values of the equilibrant F_3 and the corresponding angles ϕ and ϕ'.

Table 4.1: Resultant of two forces perpendicular to each other (Geometrical method)

F_1 (kg. wt.)	F_2 (kg. wt.)	θ	Equilibrant (Obtained experimentally)		Resultant (Calculated by adding F_1 and F_2 using Geometrical method)	
			F_3 (kg. wt.)	angle (ϕ') (degrees)	R (kg. wt.)	angle (ϕ) (degrees)
		90°				
		90°				

B. Analytical Method

Choose an appropriate Cartesian coordinate system and draw the x- and y -axes perpendicular to each other (*Fig 4.3*). In this part of the experiment, the forces F_1 and F_2 are perpendicular to each other. Let F_1 be along the x-axis and F_2 be along the y-axis. The resultant

$$R = (F_1^2 + F_2^2)^{1/2}$$

$$\varphi = \tan^{-1} (F_2/F_1)$$

Compare the calculated values of the resultant R and φ with the corresponding experimental values of the equilibrant F_3 and φ'. Enter the data in *Table 4.2*.

Table 4.2: Resultant of two forces perpendicular to each other (Analytical Method)

F_1 (kg. wt.)	F_2 (kg. wt.)	θ	Equilibrant (Measured experimentally)		Resultant (Calculated using Analytical method)	
			F_3 (kg. wt.)	angle (φ') (degrees)	Resultant $R = (F_1^2 + F_2^2)^{1/2}$ (kg. wt.)	angle $\varphi = \tan^{-1}$ (F_2/F_1) (degrees)
		90°				
		90°				

Part II. Resultant of Two Forces in Arbitrary Directions

Apply two forces F_1 and F_2 of arbitrary magnitudes along arbitrary directions. Find by trial and error the magnitude and direction of the third force F_3 (equilibrant) needed to bring the ring to an equilibrium condition. Note the magnitudes and directions of the forces F_1, F_2, and F_3.

Objective

Find the resultant of the two forces F_1 and F_2 acting at arbitrary directions in a plane using (a) the geometrical method and (b) the analytical method and compare the values with the experimentally measured values of the equilibrant.

A. Geometrical Method

Choose an appropriate scale and draw AB parallel to F_1 and the length of AB equal to the magnitude of the force to a suitable scale (*Fig 4.4*). Similarly, draw BC such that BC is parallel to the force F_2 and the length of BC is equal to the magnitude of F_2 to the same scale. Ensure that the tail of BC matches with the tip of AB. Complete the parallelogram. The diagonal AC in magnitude and direction gives the resultant of the forces F_1, and F_2 . Measure the length of the diagonal AC and calculate its magnitude. Measure the angle φ. This gives the resultant R of the vectors $F_1 + F_2$. Note the experimental values you have obtained for the equilibrant F_3 and the angle φ' it makes with respect to the negative x-axis. You will compare the magnitudes of **R** and F_3 and their directions φ and φ'. If they are equal within the experimental errors, then the geometrical method of addition of vectors is verified. Enter the data in *Table 4.3*. Note that the equilibrant will have the same line of action as the resultant R but will be oppositely directed.

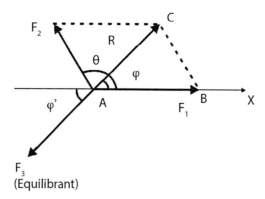

Figure 4.4: Resultant of two forces acting in arbitrary directions at a point in a plane using geometric method.

Table 4.3: Resultant of two forces applied in arbitrary directions (Geometrical method)

F_1 (kg. wt.)	F_2 (kg. wt.)	θ degrees	Equilibrant (Measured experimentally)		Resultant (Calculated using Geometrical method)	
			F_3 (kg. wt.)	angle (φ') (degrees)	Resultant R (kg. wt.)	angle (φ) (degrees)

B. Analytical Method

Choose an appropriate Cartesian coordinate system and draw the approximate directions of F_1 and F_2 and mark the corresponding angles as shown in *Fig 4.5*. Let θ_2 be the angle F_2 makes with respect to the negative x-axis as shown. If you have measured the angle θ, F_2 makes with respect to F_1, subtract this angle from 180° to get the angle θ_2 with respect to the negative x-axis. You do not have to draw F_2 using a protractor. If you draw the arrow at the approximate angle in the correct quadrant, this will serve the purpose.

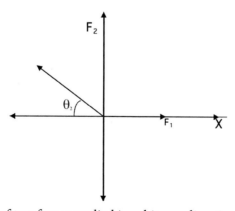

Figure 4.5: Resultant of two forces applied in arbitrary directions (Analytical method).

$$F_{1x} = F_1$$

$$F_{1y} = 0$$

$$F_{2x} = -F_2 \cos \theta_2$$

$$F_{2y} = + F_2 \sin \theta_2$$

The resultant R is given by

$$F_{Rx} = F_{1x} + F_{2x} = F_1 - F_2 \cos \theta_2$$

$$F_{Ry} = + F_2 \sin \theta_2$$

$$R = \sqrt{F_{Rx}^2 + F_{Ry}^2} \quad and \quad \phi = \tan^{-1}\left(\frac{F_{Ry}}{F_{Rx}}\right)$$

Compare the values of the resultant as obtained from the above calculations with the corresponding values of the equilibrant. Enter the data in *Table 4.4*.

Table 4.4: Resultant of two forces applied in arbitrary directions (Analytical method)

F_1 (kg. wt.)	F_2 (kg. wt.)	θ degrees	Equilibrant (Measured experimentally)		θ_2	$\sin \theta_2$	$\cos \theta_2$	Resultant (Calculated using Analytical method)	
			F_3 (kg. wt.)	angle (φ') (degrees)				Resultant R (kg. wt.)	angle (φ) (degrees)

Part III. Resultant of Three Forces in Arbitrary Directions (Optional)

Apply three forces F_1, F_2, and F_3 in arbitrary directions and of arbitrary magnitudes. By trial and error, find the force F_4 needed in magnitude and direction to bring the ring to an equilibrium condition. Note the magnitudes and directions of the forces F_1, F_2, F_3 and F_4.

Objective

Find the resultant of three forces F_1 and F_2 and F_3 acting at arbitrary directions in a plane using (a) the geometrical method and (b) the analytical method and compare the values with the experimentally measured values of the equilibrant.

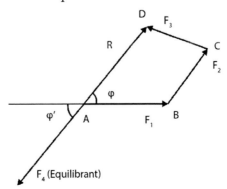

Figure 4.6: Resultant of three forces acting in arbitrary directions

A. Geometrical Method

Draw AB, BC, and CD to a suitable scale representing the forces F_1, F_2, and F_3 as detailed in Parts I and II. The vector AD gives in magnitude and direction the resultant of the three forces F_1, F_2, and F_3. Compare the values of the resultant R with the corresponding values of the equilibrant. Enter the data in *Table 4.5*. Note that the equilibrant will have the same line of action as that of R but will be oppositely directed.

Table 4.5: Resultant of three forces applied in arbitrary directions (Geometrical method)

F_1 (kg. wt.)	F_2 (kg. wt.)	F_3 (kg. wt.)	Equilibrant (Measured experimentally)		Resultant (Calculated using Geometrical method)	
			F_4 (kg. wt.)	angle (φ') (degrees)	Resultant R (kg. wt.)	angle (φ) (degrees)

B. Analytical Method

Choose an appropriate Cartesian coordinate system, draw F_1, F_2, and F_3 approximately in the direction of the respective forces, and note their angles as shown in *Fig 4.7*. Calculate the resultant R and its direction. Let us assume F_4 is the equilibrant. The resultant R and the equilibrant F_4 will have the same line of action but will be oppositely directed. Compare the values of the magnitude of the resultant R with the magnitude of the equilibrant F_4. Also compare the angle φ of the resultant with the φ' of the equilibrant. Enter the data in *Table 4.6*.

Please note that we have chosen to measure the angles theta 1, theta 2, and theta 3 all with respect to either positive or negative x axis as shown in *Fig 4.7*. Be careful about the proper positive/negative signs of the components.

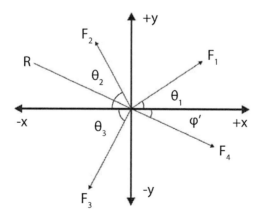

Figure 4.7: Resolving the vectors into their components in a two dimensional plane.

$$F_{1x} = + F_1 \cos \theta_1$$

$$F_{2x} = -F_2 \cos \theta_2$$

$$F_{3x} = - F_3 \cos \theta_3$$

$$F_{1y} = + F_1 \sin \theta_1$$

$$F_{2y} = +F_2 \sin \theta_2$$

$$F_{3y} = - F_3 \sin \theta_3$$

$$F_{Rx} = F_{1x} + F_{2x} + F_{3x} = F_1 \cos \theta_1 - F_2 \cos \theta_2 - F_3 \cos \theta_3$$

$$F_{Ry} = F_{1y} + F_{2y} + F_{3y} = F_1 \sin \theta_1 + F_2 \sin \theta_2 - F_3 \sin \theta_3$$

$$R = \sqrt{F_{Rx}^2 + F_{Ry}^2} \quad and \quad \phi = \tan^{-1}\left(\frac{F_{Ry}}{F_{Rx}}\right)$$

Table 4.6: Resultant of three forces applied in arbitrary directions (Analytical method)

F_1 (kg. wt.)	F_2 (kg. wt.)	F_3 (kg. wt.)	Equilibrant (Measured experimentally)		θ_2	θ_2	θ_2	Resultant (Calculated using Analytical method)	
			F_4 (kg. wt.)	angle (φ') (degrees)				Resultant R (kg. wt.)	angle (φ) (degrees)

You can also employ the electronic spreadsheets such as Excel to perform addition, subtraction, and multiplication of the forces using the Analytical Method.

V. Questions

1. Discuss how and why the following physical quantities would or would not affect your measurements and their possible relative contribution of errors to your measurements. Also, comment on how you would try to minimize those errors and correct for them.

   a. friction in the pulleys

   b. finite mass of the pulleys

   c. forces due to the strings are not perpendicular to the tangent to the ring at that point

   d. difficult to judge whether the ring is perfectly horizontal

   e. the ring and all the threads are not in the same plane

   f. the force table is not perfectly horizontal

2. When an object is in equilibrium under the action of three coplanar and concurrent forces, show that the forces form a closed triangle.

Projectile Motion in Two Dimensions

Experiments 6 and 7

I.   Introduction

In Experiment 3, you investigated the motion of a body (picket fence) in one dimension. As you dropped the picket fence through the photo-gate, the motion of the picket fence was approximately in the vertical plane. The photo-gate sampled the motion of the picket fence in one dimension, i.e., along the y-axis. In the present experiment, you will study the kinematics of a ball experiencing two-dimensional motion. Some examples of two-dimensional motion are the trajectories of a baseball when you hit the ball with a bat, a shell fired from a cannon at an angle with the horizontal, a leap for a long jump, a ball thrown at an angle with the vertical. In all these cases, you can treat the motion as two-dimensional if you neglect the spin and the sideways drift.

II.   Theory

Projectile Motion

Consider a ball launched with an initial velocity of $\mathbf{v}_0$ directed at an angle θ with the horizontal. Let us choose a coordinate system such that the trajectory of the ball always remains in the x-y plane. For simplicity, let the origin of the coordinate system coincide with the point at which the ball was launched (see Fig. 5.1)

If we neglect the effects due to air resistance, which are small for dense objects, the only force acting on the ball is the gravitational force. This results in an acceleration that is directed towards the center of the Earth or, in simple words, directed downwards. In the coordinate system we had chosen, the acceleration due to gravity would be directed along the negative y-axis. The acceleration due to gravity, g, will not have any effect on the horizontal displacement and the horizontal velocity of the ball. The acceleration due to gravity, which is a vector quantity, will not have a component perpendicular to its direction. Therefore, the horizontal component of the velocity remains unchanged throughout its motion.

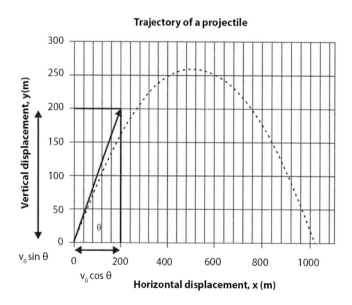

Figure 5.1: Trajectory of a particle projected with an initial velocity of 200 m/s at an angle with respect to the horizontal.

We choose the origin of the coordinate system to coincide with the point of launch. We resolve v_0 into its components along the x and y-axes. The x-component will be $v_0 \cos \theta$ and the y-component will be $v_0 \sin \theta$.

If t is the time of flight, the horizontal component of the velocity remains constant and has no acceleration

$$x(t) = x_o + (v_0 \cos \theta)\, t \tag{5.1}$$

The displacement in the vertical direction has acceleration only in the vertical direction

$$y(t) = y_o + (v_0 \sin \theta)\, t - \tfrac{1}{2} gt^2 \tag{5.2}$$

The trajectory of the ball may be obtained by eliminating t between equations (5.1) and (5.2). Substitute the value of t from (Eq: 5.1) in (Eq: 5.2). Since the ball was projected from the origin, $x_o = 0$ and $y_o = 0$.

From (Eq: 5.1) putting, $x_o = 0$, we get

$$t = x/(v_0 \cos \theta)$$

Substituting in (Eq: 5.2) after putting $y_o = 0$, we get

$$y = \frac{(v_0 \sin \theta)\, x}{v_0 \cos \theta} - \frac{1}{2} g \frac{x^2}{v_0^2 \cos^2 \theta}$$

$$y = (\tan \theta)\, x - \frac{g}{2v_0^2 \cos^2 \theta}\, x^2 \tag{5.3}$$

This is of the form $y = ax + bx^2$, where a and b are constants. This is the equation of a parabola. Therefore, the trajectory of the ball will be a parabola. The trajectories of a projectile launched at different angles with respect to the horizontal are plotted in Fig. 5.2. The trajectories were calculated using (Eq: 5.3).

The Horizontal Range

The horizontal range of a projectile, R, is defined as the horizontal distance traveled by the projectile when it returns to the height at which it was originally launched.

$$y = (\tan \theta)\, x - \frac{g}{2v_0^2 \cos^2 \theta}\, x^2 \quad = 0$$

This is a quadratic equation in x: Solving for x, you will have two solutions for x. The solution $x = 0$ corresponds to the initial position, and the second solution gives

$$x = \frac{(\tan \theta)\, 2v_0^2 \cos^2 \theta}{g} = \frac{2v_0^2 \sin \theta \, \cos \theta}{g}$$

$$R = \frac{v_0^2 \sin 2\theta}{g} \tag{5.4}$$

Here, we have used the trigonometric relation $2\cos\theta \sin\theta = \sin 2\theta$. Equation 5.4 gives the horizontal range. The maximum value of $\sin 2\theta = 1$ when $2\theta = 90°$ or $\theta = 45°$. The range will be maximum when the angle of projection $\theta = 45°$. You notice that the ranges for angles that exceed or fall short of 45° by equal amounts would be same.

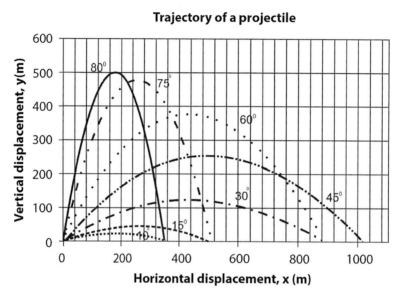

Figure 5.2: Trajectories of the projectiles launched at different angles with respect to the horizontal. The initial velocity of projection is 100 m/s. The angle of projection in degrees is given on the trajectory. The values of y are calculated for different values of x using (Eq: 5.3).

THE TIME OF FLIGHT OF AN OBJECT
LAUNCHED HORIZONTALLY IS
INDEPENDENT OF ITS INITIAL VELOCITY

I.   Objective

To investigate the time of flight of a ball launched horizontally with different initial velocities

II.   Equipment

Computer, projectile launcher, Photo-gates, meter stick, lab jack.

III.   Theory

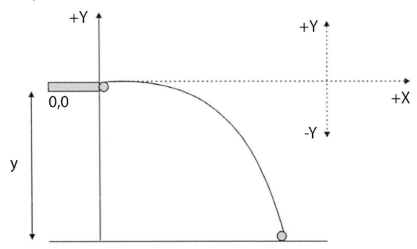

Figure 5.3: The time of flight of a projectile launched horizontally.

The position of a ball $y(t)$ as a function of time for a ball launched vertically upwards with an initial vertical velocity v_0 given by

$$y(t) = y_o + (v_0 \sin \theta) t - \tfrac{1}{2} gt^2 \qquad (5.2)$$

If you launch the ball horizontally, the vertical component of the initial velocity ($v_0 \sin \theta$) is equal to zero. (Eq: 5.2) reduces to

$$y = y_o - \tfrac{1}{2} gt^2 \qquad (5.5)$$

$$t = \left[\frac{2(y_0 - y)}{g} \right]^{1/2} \qquad (5.6)$$

The time of flight t is independent of the initial velocity v_0. The time of flight of a ball launched horizontally is a function of the distance of vertical fall ($y_0 - y$) only. The ball launched horizontally with a velocity v_0 takes the same amount of time to reach the ground as a ball that was dropped vertically from rest from the same height.

Alternatively, if we measure all the distances from the launching position and measure the vertical distances as positive downwards, (Eq: 5.5) reduces to

$$y(t) = \tfrac{1}{2} gt^2, \qquad\qquad t = \left[\frac{2y}{g} \right]^{1/2} \qquad (5.7)$$

We will use (Eq: 5.7) for all the calculations and measure the distances from the launching height as positive.

The corresponding horizontal distance traveled

$$x = v_0 t \qquad (5.8)$$

$$t = \left[\frac{2y}{g} \right]^{1/2}$$

where we have substituted the value of t from (Eq: 5.7).

The trajectory of the projectile can be easily calculated. Substituting the value of $t = x / v_o$ from (Eq: 5.8) in (Eq: 5.5) we get

$$y = + \frac{1}{2} g \frac{x^2}{v_0^2} \qquad (5.9)$$

Where y is the vertical distance traveled by the ball from the launching site as a function of x as it falls from the launching position.

IV. Experimental Details

1. Clamp the Projectile Launcher near the end of a table

2. Adjust the launcher to be horizontal

3. Attach a photo-gate to the launcher bracket

4. Connect the photo-gate at the launcher bracket to DG1 and the timer from the time-of flight apparatus to DG2.

5. Open: Logger Pro, Photo-gate, Pulse Timing

You will open a worksheet with three columns. This program has a built-in routine to calculate the velocity. You ignore the velocity column for this part of the experiment.

The column containing Δt gives you the time interval from the moment the photo-gate 1 is blocked to the moment the ball touches the pad.

For each range, launch the ball a couple of times and note the approximate position at which it touches the ground. Keep the flight pad at that place and make sure that the ball strikes the pad around the central region.

Launch the ball using the short, medium, and long-range positions and note the corresponding flight times. For each range, repeat the time measurement 3 times. Enter the data in *Table 5.1.*

Drop the ball vertically from the same height y and measure the time for the free fall.

Using PASCO Capstone/Datastudio Software

SET-UP

Open *DataStudio*, click on *create experiment* option. Attach the photo-gate to the projectile launcher, then plug the photo-gate into digital channel 1. Next, plug the receptor panel to channel 2. Click *setup* button on the top left corner. Click choose *interface* button. Select *Science Workshop 500* interface. An image will now appear in the window. Select the left most yellow highlighted port (digital channel 1). Now, select the "photo-gate" sensor option. Now select the digital channel 2 image and select the "time-of-flight accessory" sensor option. Now close the experiment setup window. Now on the top left hand corner under "data" you should have "time of flight" and "velocity" folders. When you are ready to start data collection, hit the "start" button.

DATA ANALYSIS

In order to graph time of flight you need to select the graph option under the displays menu of the bottom left hand corner. Select whichever run you want to measure under the time of flight folder and hit ok. You should see a point, which will represent the elapsed time.

Table 5.1: Time of flight measurements

| Run # | Range of the launcher | Vertical height of the nozzle from the pad y (m) | Measured time of flight (t) | | | | Calculated time of flight | % Accuracy |
			Trial I (s)	Trial II (s)	Trial III (s)	Mean of I, II and III (s)	$t = (2y/g)^{1/2}$ (s)	$\dfrac{Meas - Calc}{Calc}$ x100
1	Short range							
2	Medium range							
3	Long range							
4	Vertical free fall							

V. Questions

1. Suppose that you launched the ball at an angle of say 30° instead of 0° with the horizontal, would the time of flight be independent of the initial velocity? Explain the details.

2. Did you observe any systematic deviations between the measured and the calculated values? What are the possible sources of systematic errors in this experiment?

3. You might have observed that the time of flight for all the measurements are not identical showing possibly large variations. What are the possible reasons why there are such large variations?

PART II: RANGES OF A BALL LAUNCHED AT DIFFERENT ANGLES

I.   Objective

To measure the ranges of a ball launched at different angles with the horizontal and compare them with the calculated values.

Experimental arrangement

In this experiment, you will measure the ranges of the projectile when it returns to the height at which it was originally launched.

Put a lab jack at the landing site and adjust its height such that the launching and the landing positions are at the same height.

You will be using (Eq: 5.4) to calculate the ranges. To calculate the range, you need the values of the initial velocity v_0, and the angle of launch θ.

1.   Install one photo-gate to the bracket of the Projectile Launcher and connect them to DG1.

     Measure the diameter of the ball and enter the data in the computer. We will be measuring the time difference between blocking and unblocking of the LED sensor.

2.   Fix the angle θ at which you wish to launch the projectile (choose $\theta = 45°$, $45° \pm 10°$, $45° \pm 20°$, $45° \pm 30°$). Cock the ball and release it. Note the approximate position where the ball landed.

     You will put a lab jack at this position and adjust the height of the landing position such that it is at the same height as that of the launching position. At this position, tape a piece of white paper with a piece of carbon paper (carbon-side down). When the ball hits the carbon paper, it will leave an impression on the white paper.

3.   For each angle, measure the horizontal range and the corresponding initial velocity of the ball using the computer. The horizontal range is measured from the nozzle of the launcher to the carbon mark on the paper. Enter the data in *Table 5.2*. Repeat the measurement for 2-3 initial velocities using the different ranges on the spring loaded launcher.

Table 5.2: Ranges of a ball launched at different angles

Run #	Launcher range	Angle of launch	Initial velocity v_0 (m/s)	Measured range R (m)	Calculated range $R=(v_0^2 \sin 2\theta /g)$ (m)
1	Short Range	15°			
		25°			
		35°			
		45°			
		55°			
		65°			
		75°			
2	Medium Range	15°			
		25°			
		35°			
		45°			
		55°			
		65°			
		75°			

II.   Questions

1. For a given initial velocity of the projectile, suppose that you wanted to have a maximum horizontal range to strike a target, at what angle with the horizontal would you like to launch the projectile? Does your data support your answer?

2. Calculate the % difference between the measured and the calculated values of the ranges. Do they show any systematic errors? What are the possible systematics errors in this experiment?

TIME OF FLIGHT AND RANGE OF A PROJECTILE LAUNCHED FROM A HEIGHT AT DIFFERENT ANGLES

I.   Objective

Measure the time of flight and range of a projectile launched from a height at different angles of projection and compare them with the calculated values.

II.   Theory

In this experiment, you would measure the time of flight and the horizontal distance traveled by a projectile launched at different angles with respect to the horizontal.

The equations of motion along the y and x-axis can be separated and can be written as

$$y\,(t) - y_0 \;=\; (v_0 \sin \theta)\, t - (½)g\, t^2 \tag{5.10}$$

$$x = R = (v_0 \cos \theta)\, t \tag{5.11}$$

PART I: Time of flight measurements

OBJECTIVE

Measure the time of flight of the projectile launched with different velocities and different angles of projection using a sensor and a launching pad and compare the measured values with the values calculated using (Eq: 5.10).

EQUIPMENT

Computer, projectile launcher, Photo-gates, meter stick, lab jack.

III. Experimental Details

1. Clamp the Projectile Launcher near the end of a table

2. Attach a photo-gate to the launcher bracket

3. Connect the photo-gate at the launcher bracket to DG1 and the timer from the time-of flight apparatus to DG2.

4. Open: Logger Pro, Photo-gate, Pulse Timing

Using PASCO Capstone/Datastudio Software

SET-UP

Open *DataStudio*, click on *create experiment* option. Attach the photo-gate to the projectile launcher, then plug the photo-gate into digital channel 1. Next, plug the receptor panel to channel 2. Click *setup* button on the top left corner. Click choose *interface* button. Select *Science Workshop 500* interface. An image will now appear in the window. Select the left most yellow highlighted port (digital channel 1). Now, select the "photo-gate" sensor option. Now select the digital channel 2 image and select the "time-of-flight accessory" sensor option. Now close the experiment setup window. Now on the top left hand corner under "data" you should have "time of flight" and "velocity" folders. When you are ready to start data collection, hit the "start" button.

DATA ANALYSIS

In order to graph time of flight you need to select the graph option under the displays menu of the bottom left hand corner. Select whichever run you want to measure under the time of flight folder and hit ok. You should see a point, which will represent the elapsed time.

Measure the height y_0, the angle of projection θ and the time of flight t. Compare the measured time of flight values with the calculated values using (Eq: 5.10). Note that (Eq: 5.10) is quadratic in t, therefore you will get two values for t. Pickup the appropriate value. Enter the data in *Table 5.3*.

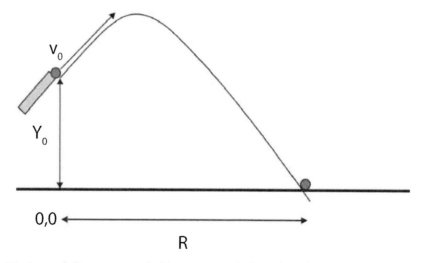

Figure 5.4: Horizontal distance traveled by a projectile launched from a height at different angles.

Table 5.3: Time of flight measurements

Run #	Launcher range	Angle of launch	Initial velocity v_0(m/s)	Measured Time of flight, t (s)	Calculated Time of flight using (Eq: 5.10) (s)	% Deviation in the measured values compared to calculated values
1	Short Range	20°				
2		30°				
3		45°				
4		60°				
5		70°				

PART II: Horizontal distance traveled by a projectile launched from a height at different angles

Using the time of flight data collected in Part I , calculate the horizontal distances traveled by the projectile and compare them with measured values. Enter the data in *Table 5.4*.

Table 5.4: Ranges of a ball launched at a height y_0 at different angles

Run #	Launcher range	Angle of launch	Vertical height of launcher from the pad (y_0) (m)	Initial velocity v_0 (m/s)	Measured Time of flight t (s)	Measured horizontal distance R (m)	Calculated Horizontal distance using Eq: 5.11 R (m)	% Accuracy Meas - Calc / Calc
1	Short Range	20°						
2		30°						
3		45°						
4		60°						
5		70°						

IV. Questions

(You give answers/comments to the following questions in your lab report)

1. For a given velocity, at what angle of projection will you have the maximum horizontal range? Can you support your answer from your experimental data?

2. Calculate the percent difference between the predicted and the calculated values of R in *Table 5.4*.

3. What are the possible sources of error in this experiment? If you were given a chance to repeat this experiment again, how would you try to improve the precision of the measurements?

4. Ranges for angles that exceed or fall short of 45° by equal amounts are the same. Prove this statement using (Eq: 5.4). Does your experimental data confirm this? Explain.

Newton's Second Law

Experiments 8, 9 & 10

I.   Introduction and Objectives

Newton's Second Law states that the rate of change of momentum of a body is equal to the net force acting on the body and will be in the direction of the net force. If m is the mass of the object, $\mathbf{v}$ is its instantaneous velocity, and F_{av} is the net force, then:

$$F_{av} = \frac{\Delta \mathbf{p}}{\Delta t} = \frac{\Delta(m\mathbf{v})}{\Delta t} = \frac{m(\Delta \mathbf{v})}{\Delta t} = m\mathbf{a}_{av}$$

Here, the mass of the object m is taken as a constant. You can get instantaneous values of the force and acceleration by taking the limit as $\Delta t \rightarrow 0$.

In this experiment, you will apply a known force **F** to an object and measure the induced acceleration **a**. You will compare the measured acceleration with the value expected from Newton's Second Law.

II.   Equipment

Air track, gliders, weights, and computer

III.   Theory

Consider two masses m_1 and m_2 connected by a light inextensible string as shown in Fig. 6.1. Assume that the frictional forces are small and can be neglected. The free body diagrams of m_1 and m_2 are also shown in Fig. 6.1. We calculate the acceleration **a** of m_2.

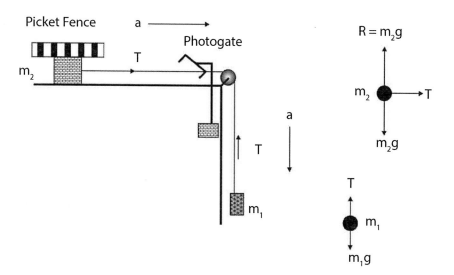

Figure 6.1: Experimental arrangement. Free-body diagrams of m_1 and m_2

Since m_1 and m_2 are connected by an inextensible light string, the total mass of the system is (m_1 + m_2). The pulley is assumed to be light and frictionless and therefore the tension in the string can be treated as an internal force. The net force acting on the system is m_1g, the acceleration of the combined mass system.

$$a = \frac{m_1 g}{(m_1 + m_2)} \qquad (6.1)$$

Alternatively, the equation of motion for m_1 is

$$m_1 g - T = m_1 a \qquad (6.2)$$

The equation of motion for m_2 is

$$T = m_2 a \qquad (6.3)$$

Substituting for T in (Eq: 6.2), we get

$$a = \frac{m_1 g}{(m_1 + m_2)} \qquad (6.4)$$

Newton's First Law states: If the net force acting on the body is equal to zero, a body at rest will remain at rest, and if the body is moving with constant velocity, it will continue moving with that constant velocity indefinitely.

In the real world, as we know, objects moving with constant velocity do not move with that velocity indefinitely, but they eventually come to rest. Why? You know that frictional forces are responsible. How can you design an experiment so that you may minimize frictional forces? The answer is to use an air track. On an air track, the objects will be moving on a gentle air cushion resulting in negligible frictional forces.

IV. Experimental Details

First, adjust the air track such that it is horizontal. You will use a level indicator for this adjustment. Adjust the airflow such that the cart moves with almost no friction. You can test this condition by very gently pushing the cart.

You will employ the picket fence to measure the displacement, the velocity and the acceleration of the cart. Using putty, fix the picket fence to the cart.

Measure the mass of the cart + putty + picket fence. This will be m_2.

Measure the mass of the hanger + mass of the weights added. This will be m_1.

Position and adjust the photo-gate for measuring the displacement, the velocity, and the acceleration of mass m_2 using the motion detection software and picket fence. Hold mass m_2 so that the system is stationary. Release m_2 gently and let the picket fence pass through the photo-gate. The photo-gate may be positioned anywhere along the route of m_2.

Repeat the measurements for different values of m_1 and m_2. you can change the values of m_2 by adding or removing additional weights to the glider. Make sure that the additional weights are distributed equally on both sides of the glider. Enter the data in *Table 6.1*.

Using PASCO Capstone/Datastudio Software

SET-UP

Open *DataStudio*, click on *create experiment* option. Attach the photo-gate to the projectile launcher, then plug the photo-gate into digital channel 1. Next, plug the receptor panel to channel 2. Click *setup* button on the top left corner. Click choose *interface* button. Select *Science Workshop 500* interface. An image will now appear in the window. Select the left most yellow highlighted port (digital channel 1). Now select the "Photo-gate and Picket Fence" sensor option. Select the "Constants" tab and set your band spacing on the picket fence. Close the experiment setup window. Now on the top left hand corner under "data" you should have position, velocity, and acceleration folders. When you are ready to start data collection hit the "start" button. After you are done collecting data, hit the "stop" button.

DATA ANALYSIS

To graph the acceleration, select the graph option in the display menu. Chose the run you want to graph under the acceleration folder and hit ok. Then choose the correct fit for the data.

Table 6.1: Experimental verification of Newton's second law

Run #	m_1 (kg)	m_2 (kg)	Measured acceleration a_{meas} (m/s^2)	Calculated acceleration $a_{cal} = m_1 g/(m_1 + m_2)$ (m/s^2)	Percent deviation $((a_{meas} - a_{cal})/a_{cal})$ x 100
1					
2					
3					
4					
5					
6					

Enter the measured values of m_1, m_2, and a in the worksheet of the Excel program and complete the required calculations.

You will submit the following along with your lab report.

1. A printout of the displacement, velocity, and acceleration measurements

2. A final table where the experimental and calculated values of the acceleration are compared. This will be an output of the excel program worksheet.

V. Questions

1. What is the effect of the gravitational force on m_2 and its motion? In what way does the gravitational force on m_2 affect your experiment?

2. Are the values of a_{cal} and a_{meas} equal? Identify the possible sources of error in a_{exp} and explain how you would try to minimize them.

3. If you keep the photo-gate at a different position along the path of m_2, do you expect to get different values for the measured acceleration, a_{meas}? Explain?

I.   Introduction

Atwood's machine is a simple device that has been traditionally employed to measure the acceleration due to gravity 'g'. This has been a great device particularly when time measurements were carried out by manually employing stop watches. By using a stop watch, it is impossible to measure correctly the acceleration of a freely falling body. In the case of Atwood's machine, one suspends two unequal masses over a pulley so that the net acceleration of the system is less than the acceleration due to gravity. Now that the acceleration due to gravity can be directly measured by timing a freely falling body using photo-gates, Atwood's machine is not that popular for the measurement of acceleration due to gravity. However, Atwood's machine provides an experimental arrangement where one can vary the acceleration of the system by changing the masses and measure it.

II.   Objectives

Measure the acceleration due to gravity using an Atwood's machine

III.   Theory

Any object of mass, m, near the Earth experiences a force of mg directed towards the center of the Earth; on Earth's surface, the object will experience an acceleration of 9.81 m/s² towards the earth. If you connect two masses, m_1 and m_2, as shown in the Fig. 6.2 by means of a light, inextensible string passing over a frictionless pulley of negligible mass, you can easily calculate the acceleration of the system. In this experiment, you will measure the acceleration of the coupled masses to calculate the acceleration due to gravity. The tension in the string is an internal force when you consider the motion of the entire system and not the individual motions of the masses.

The net force acting on the system = $(m_2 - m_1)g$ (The tension is an internal force.)

If m_2 is moving downwards with an acceleration a, m_1 will be moving upwards with an acceleration of the same magnitude.

The total mass of the system = $(m_1 + m_2)$

The acceleration of the system = the net force acting on the system / Total mass of the system

$a = (m_2 - m_1)\, g/ (m_1 + m_2)$

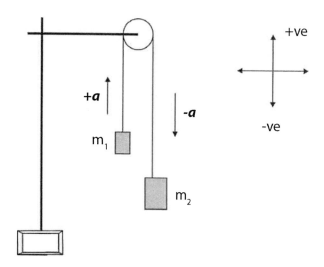

Figure 6.2: Schematic of the Atwood machine arrangement.

By measuring the values of m_1, m_2, and a , one can calculate the acceleration due to gravity g. To measure the acceleration a, you will design a simple picket fence type arrangement yourself. Alternatively, you may use a smart pulley with a photo-gate arrangement; this gives the acceleration of the system directly.

IV. Experimental Details

Take a fine thread and connect two weight hangers as shown in Fig. 6.2. In order to measure the acceleration a of the system, you will design a simple picket fence type arrangement. Take black tape, which is available in most labs for electrical insulation purposes, and connect three strips to the thread with equal spacing between them. Make sure that all the black strips move in the same plane as the weight moves up or down. If necessary, connect the strips by means of a transparent cello tape or a thin plastic sheet that will keep them in the same plane. Arrange a photo-gate such that the black tape intersects the light as the masses move up or down.

Using PASCO Capstone/Datastudio Software

SET-UP

Open *DataStudio*, click on *create experiment* option. Plug the photo-gate into digital channel 1. Click *setup* button on the top left corner. Click *choose interface* button. Select *Science Workshop 500* interface. An image will now appear in the window. Select the left most yellow highlighted port (digital channel 1). Now select the "Photo-gate and Picket Fence" sensor option. Select the "Constants" tab and set your band spacing. Now close the experiment setup window. Now on the top left hand corner under "data" you should have position, velocity, and acceleration folders. When you are ready to start data collection hit the "start" button. After you are done collecting data, hit the "stop" button.

DATA ANALYSIS

To graph the acceleration, select the graph option in the display menu. Chose the run you want to graph under the acceleration folder and hit ok. Then choose the correct fit for the data.

Table 6.2: Acceleration due to gravity using Atwood's machine

Run #	m_1 (kg)	m_2 (kg)	$(m_2 - m_1)$ (kg)	$(m_1 + m_2)$ (kg)	Measured acceleration a (m/s²)	Calculated acceleration $(m_2 - m_1)\, g / (m_1 + m_2)$ (m/s²)
1						
2						
3						
4						
5						
6						

Plot a graph with the measured acceleration along the *y*-axis and $((m_2 - m_1) / (m_1 + m_2))$ along the *x*-axis. Fit the data to a straight line. The slope of the curve gives you the acceleration due to gravity.

V. Questions

1. Assume that you fixed the picket fence arrangement at a different place on the thread. Would you get a different value for the acceleration? Explain.

2. If you keep equal masses in both the arms of the Atwood's machine, what will be the acceleration of the system?

3. The measured value of the acceleration a, is less than the acceleration due to gravity. On what factors does the value of the acceleration of the system depend? What will be the minimum value of the acceleration a, of the system and how would you achieve it? Under what limiting conditions will the system have acceleration equal to the value of g: the acceleration due to gravity?

4. From your data, did you observe any systematic errors? Identify the possible sources of such systematic errors?

5. We have assumed that the mass of the pulley is negligible. If the mass of the pulley was not negligible, how would this affect the acceleration a, of the system? How would this effect conservation of mechanical energy within the system?

6. Suppose that the mass m_1 moved a distance d upwards. Write down the conservation of mechanical energy for the system in the form of an equation. Remember to take the finite mass of the pulley into account.

Note: This experiment may be preformed employing three different experimental arrangements:

1. Using a picket fence type arrangement,

2. Using a smart pulley arrangement and

3. Using a motion detector.

CENTRIPETAL FORCE

I.   Introduction

If an object is to move in a circular orbit or along the arc of a circle, it must be provided with a centripetal force (a center-seeking force) to keep it moving along the arc of the circle. In the absence of a centripetal force, an object at that instant would fly off along the tangent of its path and would not take a circular path.

When you exit the freeway to a sharp ramp, you notice a speed limit sign. On the ramp, the centripetal force needed to complete the semi-circular path is provided by the frictional forces between the tires and the road and the banking of the road. If you exceed the speed limit, there is a good chance that you may not be able to make the curve! As the Earth orbits around the sun, the centripetal force needed to keep the Earth in its orbit is provided by the gravitational attractive force between the sun and the Earth. As electrons orbit around a nucleus, the centripetal force needed to keep the electrons in orbit is provided by the electrostatic forces which are attractive for unlike charges. In this experiment, you will measure the centripetal force needed to keep an object moving in a circular orbit at constant speed, and you will also measure the centripetal force's dependence on the mass of the object, the object's speed and the radius of the orbit.

OBJECTIVES

To investigate the dynamics of an object executing uniform circular motion. To study the centripetal force needed to keep the object in uniform circular motion and its dependence on: (1) the mass of the object, (2) the radius of the circular path, and (3) the speed of the object.

II.   Equipment/Materials

Centripetal force apparatus (PASCO ME-8952), rotation platform (PASCO ME-8951), balance, mass and hanger set, string

III.   Theory

Uniform Circular Motion: If an object is moving with a constant speed along the arc of a circle then the object is said to have uniform circular motion. In this case, the speed is constant although the velocity is changing continuously. The change in the velocity is the result of the centripetal force provided to the object to keep it going in a circular path. The magnitude of the centripetal force

$$F_c = \frac{mv^2}{r} \tag{6.5}$$

Where m is the mass of the object, v is its speed and r is the radius of the circular path. The centripetal force F_c needed to keep the mass moving in uniform circular motion is: (1) directly proportional to its mass, (2) directly proportional to the square of its tangential speed, and (3) inversely proportional to the radius of the circular orbit.

The centripetal force may be expressed in terms of the angular velocity, ω. Since $v = \omega r$

$$F_c = m\, r\, \omega^2$$

If f is the corresponding frequency in Hz (cycles/second), and since $\omega = 2\,\pi f$, the centripetal force

$$F_c = 4\pi^2 m\, r\, f^2$$

If T is the time period, that is, the time the object takes to complete one revolution, the linear speed of the object

$$v = \frac{2\,\pi r}{T}$$

Substituting for v in (Eq: 6.5), the centripetal force may be expressed in the form

$$F_c = \frac{4\pi^2 mr}{T2} \tag{6.6}$$

From (Eq: 6.5), the centripetal acceleration

$$a_c = \frac{v^2}{r}$$

The centripetal acceleration is also directed towards the center of the circle.

IV. Experimental

Part I Variation of the centripetal force, F_c, with the mass, m, of the object. In this part of the experiment, the speed and the radius will be kept constant.

Assemble the centripetal force apparatus as per the details presented in the PASCO manual. Fix the center post assembly at the center of the rotating platform and the side post assembly at a convenient distance from the center, say 15 cm. Introduce about 200g on the hanging mass holder. Adjust the position of the indicator bracket such that it is at the level of the indicator disk. The spring is stretched because of the gravitational force (mg) of the hanging mass.

Remove the hanging mass, the clamp-on pulley and the thread connecting to the mass, M. When the hanging weight is removed, the spring will be pulled back (upwards) since the applied force Mg is removed.

Rotate the platform at a constant rate such that the indicator disk is at the same level as the indicator bracket. The spring is pulled downwards because you have to provide the rotating mass m the necessary centripetal force. The centripetal force needed is to be provided externally to keep the object experiencing circular motion. The reaction force will be equal and opposite of the centripetal force; because of this, the spring will be pulled downwards. When the indicator disk is at the same level as the indicator bracket, the magnitude of the centripetal force is equal to the magnitude of Mg. Maintain this speed by rotating the rough region of the shaft below the rotating platform. It may not be possible to maintain the indicator disk at the same level particularly when you are rotating the platform manually. If the indicator disk is moving up and down with respect to the indicator bracket, adjust the speed of the rotating platform such that the pink reference disk is approximately equal amounts of time above and below the reference platform.

Keeping the speed of the platform approximately constant, note the time for, say, ten revolutions using a stop clock. You may keep a vertical rod or stand which would act as a reference for counting the number of oscillations. The better way is to hook up the photo-gate attachment and measure the angular velocity.

Change the mass by removing the side disks one at a time. For each mass, by rotating the platform at a uniform rate, find the condition when the pink indicator disk is at the same level as the indicator bracket. Note the time for ten oscillations. Enter data in *Table 6.3*.

Table 6.3: Experimental determination of centripetal force

Run #	Mass of the object m (kg)	Time for 10 oscillation s (s)	Time period T (s)	Radius r (m)	Experimental centripetal force from (Eq: 6.6) $(4\pi^2 mr)/T^2$ (N)	Expected Centripetal force = Mg (N)

The radius r is measured from the center of the platform to the central position of the rotating mass.

1. Plot a curve between m (y-axis) and T^2 (x- axis). Fit the data to a straight-line curve. What will the slope of the curve correspond to? Obtain the value of the centripetal force F_c from the fitted value of the slope.

Part II - Centripetal force and its dependence on the speed of the object. In this part of the experiment mass and the radius will be kept constant.

Part III - Centripetal force and its dependence on the radius of the circle. In this part of the experiment mass and the speed will be kept constant.

Friction

Experiments 11, 12, 13, 14 & 15

I.   Introduction and Objectives

Whenever a body is moving on a surface frictional forces act between the two surfaces such as to oppose the motion of the bodies. Frictional forces play an important role in our everyday lives. Frictional forces allow us to walk, run, write, ride vehicles on the road etc. and often, we try to increase frictional forces by using special materials or coating ordinary surfaces with such materials. Frictional forces also reduce the efficiency of machines and, one tries to minimize the frictional forces by using lubricants and ball bearings. In this experiment, we will investigate the nature of the so-called frictional forces acting on solid surfaces.

II.   Theory

Consider a block on a table. If you look at the interfaces of the block and the table at high magnification, you will find that the contacting surfaces have random protrusions. When you try to move the block relative to the table, the obstructions caused by the protrusions oppose the motion. The obstructions or the protrusions exist even when the surfaces seem to be quite smooth and polished. At a microscopic level, the electrostatic forces between atoms/molecules are responsible for the forces opposing the motion. It is difficult to work out the complex way the electrostatic forces act between the surfaces in contact from a microscopic point of view. However, they have simple and predictable behavior when you look at the effects on the motion of the body from a macroscopic point of view. The macroscopic effects of these forces are known in general as frictional forces. It should be stated that the frictional forces are not fundamental forces of interaction between atoms/molecules. In this experiment, you will investigate the nature of the frictional forces from a macroscopic point of view.

Consider, say, a wooden block of mass m on a table (see Fig. 7.1). The forces acting on the block are shown in the free body diagram. Since there is no acceleration of the block perpendicular to the table, the normal reaction force is equal in magnitude and opposite to the gravitational force. We apply a variable horizontal force F (see Fig. 7.2) by connecting the block to a force probe and pulling it. For low values of force, the block will not move because the net force acting on the block is zero. Since the block is not moving, the frictional force is equal in magnitude to the applied force but opposite in direction. The frictional forces are always directed such that they oppose the motion of the object. Until the object is set into motion, the frictional force adjusts itself such that the magnitude of the frictional force is equal in magnitude to the applied force but opposite in direction.

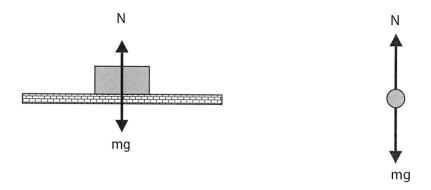

Figure 7.1: A block at rest on a table and its free body diagram

If the magnitude of the force, F, is gradually increased, at some value of F, the block barely moves. If the net acceleration of the block is close to zero, then the net force acting on the block is approximately equal to zero. Under these conditions, the magnitude of the static frictional force f_s is equal to the magnitude of the applied force and is in opposite direction. When this condition is satisfied, if you tap the table or if you give a very gentle push to the block, the block will be accelerated in the direction of the applied force. From a number of experiments, it has been observed that the magnitude of the frictional force f_s is proportional to the force with which the body presses the surface. The frictional force is proportional to the normal reaction

$$f_s \propto N$$

$$f_s = \mu_s N$$

$$(7.1)$$

Here, μ_s is a dimensionless proportionality constant and is called the coefficient of static friction. If the object is already in motion, the applicable frictional force is known as the kinetic frictional force. In general, the coefficient of kinetic friction for the same set of bodies is less than the coefficient of static friction. The kinetic frictional force is also proportional to the normal reaction force, N

$$f_k \propto N$$

$$f_k = \mu_k N$$

$$(7.2)$$

where μ_k is the coefficient of kinetic friction.

The coefficients of static and kinetic friction depend on the nature of the materials in contact. The values of μ_s and μ_k for some materials are given in *Table 7.1.*

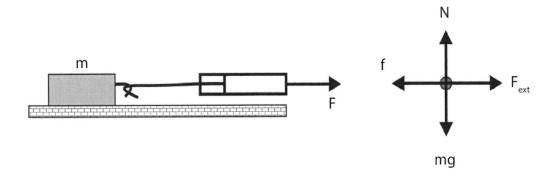

Figure 7.2: A mass *m* pulled by an external force **F** and its free body diagram.

Table 7.1: Coefficients of static and dynamic frictions for some materials

Material	Coefficient of static friction (μ_s)	Coefficient of kinetic friction (μ_k)
Wood on wood	0.5	0.3
Ice on ice	0.05-0.15	0.02
Steel on ice	0.1	0.05
Lubricated ball bearings	<0.01	<0.01
Synovial joints (human limbs)	0.01	0.01
Rubber(Tires) on dry concrete	1.0	0.7 − 0.8
Rubber (Tires) on wet concrete	0.7	0.5
Teflon on Teflon	0.04	0.04
Glass on glass	0.9	0.4

Experimentally, it was observed that the frictional forces in general

1. do not depend on the smoothness or roughness of the surfaces in contact

2. do not depend on the surface area of contact

3. are directly proportional to the force pressing the surfaces together, i.e., the normal force pressing the interface.

4. are independent of the speed (for normal speeds) with which the object is sliding.

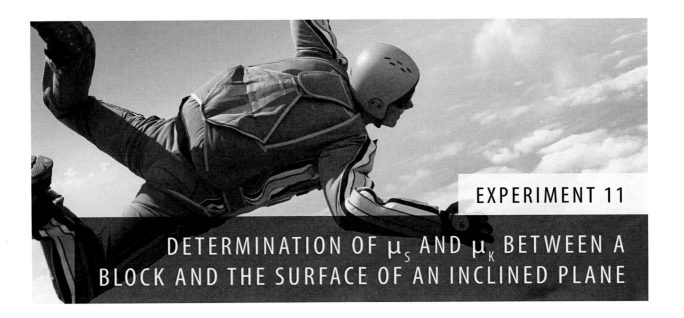

DETERMINATION OF μ_S AND μ_K BETWEEN A BLOCK AND THE SURFACE OF AN INCLINED PLANE

Part I
Determination of μ_s and μ_k by Sliding a Block on a Table

OBJECTIVE

To determine the coefficient of static friction μ_s between a wooden block and a table

A. Determination of μ_s, between a wooden block and a table

In this experiment, you will fix a light pulley at the edge of a table as shown in Fig. 7.3. Connect a wooden block by means of an inextensible string to a weight hanger suspended at the edge of the table. You will increase the weight on the hanger gradually until the wooden block barely moves. When this condition is satisfied, the static frictional force is equal to the gravitational force of the weight (Mg).

1. The experimental arrangement is shown in Fig. 7.3. Clean the surfaces of the block and the table using a tissue. Make sure that the string is parallel to the surface of the table

2. Gradually add weights to the hanger such that m_b barely moves when you *do not tap* on the table. Find the weight Mg necessary to barely move m_b

3. Add weights (m_w) to the wooden block and repeat the procedure in (2) such that ($m_b + m_w$) barely moves

4. Enter the data in **Table 7.2**

5. Transfer the data to the worksheet of the Excel program and plot the static frictional force f_s (= Mg) on the y-axis vs. the normal reaction force on the block = ($m_b + m_w$)g on the x-axis.

6. Fit the data to a straight-line curve. The slope of the straight line gives the coefficient of static friction.

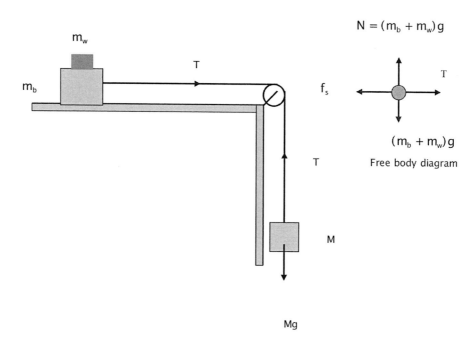

$$N = (m_b + m_w)g$$

Free body diagram

Figure 7.3: Experimental arrangement.

Table 7.2: Determination of the coefficient of static friction (μ_s) between a wooden block and a table

Run #	m_b (kg)	m_w (kg)	$(m_b + m_w)$ (kg)	Normal reaction $N = (m_b + m_w)g$	Mass (M)	Static frictional force $f_s = Mg$	Coefficient of static friction $\mu_s = f_s/N = \dfrac{M}{m_b + m_w}$
1							
2							
3							
4							
5							
6							

Average value of the coefficient of static friction (μ_s) =

Coefficient of static friction from the graph (μ_s) =

Coefficient of static friction from *Table 7.1* for the surfaces studied =

B. Determination of μ_K BETWEEN a wooden bock and a table

1. The experimental arrangement is the same as shown in Fig. 7.3

2. Adjust the mass M such that the wooden block and the weight moves with a constant velocity when you give a very gentle push to the wooden block or when you tap on the table

When the block is moving with a constant velocity, i.e., no acceleration, the net force acting on the body is equal to zero. When this condition is satisfied,

Applied force = kinetic frictional force

Enter the value of M in *Table 7.3*.

Table 7.3: Determination of the coefficient of kinetic friction (μ_k)

Run #	m_b (kg)	m_w (kg)	$(m_b + m_w)$ (kg)	Normal reaction $N = (m_b + m_w) g$	Kinetic frictional force $f_k = F = Mg$	Coefficient of kinetic friction $\mu_k = f_k/N = Mg/N$
1						
2						
3						
4						
5						
6						

Average value of the coefficient of kinetic friction (μ_k) =

Coefficient of kinetic friction from the graph (μ_k) =

Coefficient of kinetic friction from *Table 7.1* for the surfaces studied =

Alternative Procedure: Obtain the condition for static friction as in Part I. If you give a gentle push to the wooden block, you would notice that the block would be moving with acceleration, and the speed of the block gradually increasing. Gradually reduce the mass M until you reach the condition when the block will be moving with a constant velocity and is not accelerating. Enter the data in *Table 7.3*. For different weights added to the wooden block, find the corresponding values of M, and enter the data in *Table 7.3*. Transfer the data to an Excel program and plot kinetic frictional force ($f_k = Mg$) on the y-axis vs. normal reaction force ($m_b + m_w$) g on the x-axis. The slope of the best-fitted straight line gives the coefficient of kinetic friction μ_k.

How do you make certain that the acceleration of the block is equal to or close to zero?

Using putty, fix the picket fence on the wooden block as shown in Fig. 6.1. Arrange a photo-gate and measure the acceleration to the third decimal place. Try to obtain the condition that the acceleration of the block is close to zero and is moving with constant velocity. In this case, the normal force would be $(m_b + m_w + m_{pf})$ g. Where, m_{pf} is the mass of the picket fence plus putty used to fix the picket fence on to the wooden block. If the wooden block is wobbling and not moving in a straight line use a motion detector.

Part II
Determination of μ_s and μ_k by Sliding the Block on an Inclined Plane

A. Determination of μ_s using an inclined plane

I.   Introduction and Objectives

For this experiment, you will employ an inclined plane where the angle of inclination can be continuously changed. If you have a block on the inclined plane, and if the angle of inclination is gradually increased, at some angular position, the component of the gravitational force along the plane is equal and opposite to the static frictional force. When this condition is satisfied, from the measured value of the angle θ, one can calculate the coefficient of static friction.

II.   Equipment

Inclined plane apparatus, wooden block

III.   Theory

Consider a block of mass m on an inclined plane. Let the angle of inclination of the inclined plane be θ. The forces acting on the block are gravitational force mg acting vertically downwards and the normal reaction force N perpendicular to the surface of the inclined plane. We resolve mg into two components one along the inclined plane and the other perpendicular to the plane. The component along the inclined plane will be ($mg \sin \theta$) and the component perpendicular to the plane will be ($mg \cos \theta$). Since there is no acceleration perpendicular to the plane, the normal reaction $N = mg \cos \theta$. The component mg sin θ will be pulling the block along the inclined plane whereas the static frictional force will be in a direction opposite to it. The block will be in equilibrium as long as the net force acting on the block is equal to zero. As you gradually increase the angle θ, for a certain value of θ, the force mg sin θ, barely exceeds the maximum value of the frictional force when it just starts sliding downwards. The forces acting on the body and their components along and perpendicular to the inclined plane are shown in Fig. 7.4.

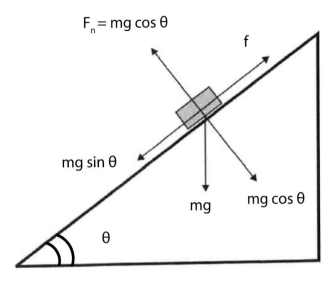

$F_n = mg \cos \theta$

f

$mg \sin \theta$

mg

$mg \cos \theta$

θ

Figure 7.4: Forces acting on a block on an inclined plane.

IV. Experimental

Keep the wooden block on an inclined plane and gradually raise the inclination such that the block starts barely slipping. Do not tap the inclined plane or push the block. When it is barely slipping, the net force on the block is zero.

$$mg \sin \theta = \mu_s \, mg \cos \theta$$

$$\mu_s = \tan \theta \tag{7.3}$$

Measure the value of θ. Repeat the experiment several times and enter the data in *Table 7.4*.

Table 7.4: Determination of the coefficient of static friction using an inclined plane

Run #	θ (degrees)	tan θ	measured μ_s (= tanθ)	Accepted value from Table 7.1 (μ_s)

Average value of the coefficient of static friction μ_s =

Accepted value =

$$\% \text{ Accuracy } = \frac{\text{Measured value - Accepted value}}{\text{Accepted value}} \times 100$$

B. Determination of μ_k Using an Inclined Plane

V. Experimental

As in the preceding part, put the wooden block on the inclined plane. This time you will be gradually raising the inclination of the inclined plane each time by gently tapping the inclined plane or by giving a very gentle push to the block. Find out the condition when the block moves with a constant velocity with no acceleration. When this condition is satisfied,

$mg \sin \theta = \mu_k \, mg \cos \theta$

$\mu_k = \tan \theta$

Repeat the experiment several times and enter the data in *Table 7.5.*

Table 7.5: Determination of the coefficient of kinetic friction using an inclined plane

Run #	θ	$\tan \theta$	measured $\mu_k \ (= \tan\theta)$	Accepted value from Table 7.1 (μ_k)

Average value of the coefficient of static friction μ_k =

Accepted value =

$$\% \text{ Accuracy } = \frac{\text{Measured value - Accepted value}}{\text{Accepted value}} \times 100$$

VI. Questions

1. Do your experimental data support that in general $\mu_s > \mu_K$. Give logical reasons why you would expect $\mu_s > \mu_K$.

2. Can you cite a couple of examples from our daily experiences where we notice that $\mu_s > \mu_K$?

3. It is stated that the frictional force depends on the normal force. From the experimental data you collected, can you draw this conclusion? Give details.

4. Experimentally observed qualitative features of the frictional forces are given in the text, Section 7, p. 118. Give your explanations as why each of them seem to be logical, or perhaps not, from your perspective?

DETERMINATION OF μ_k BY MEASURING THE DECELERATION OF A BLOCK USING A MOTION DETECTOR

I. Introduction and Objectives

The experimental arrangement is shown in Fig. 7.5. If you give a push (impulsive force) to the wooden block and leave it, it will acquire a certain initial velocity. After acquiring a certain maximum velocity, the block will start decelerating because of the frictional force opposing its motion. By measuring the deceleration of the wooden block using the motion detector and knowing the mass of the wooden block, the magnitude of the frictional force and hence the coefficient of kinetic friction can be calculated.

OBJECTIVE

To determine the coefficient of kinetic friction of a block using a motion detector

II. Equipment

Motion detector, wooden block, PC

III. Theory

Consider a block of mass m on a table. If you give a push to the block and leave it, it will acquire a certain initial maximum velocity and then get decelerated. Because of the frictional forces, the block will experience a constant deceleration. Using a motion detector, one can measure the displacement of the block as a function of time and obtain the value of the deceleration. Knowing the deceleration, one can calculate the kinetic frictional force and the coefficient of kinetic friction.

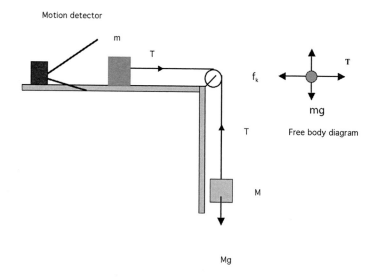

Figure 7.5: Determination of μ_k by measuring the deceleration of a block using a motion detector.

IV. Experimental

Keep the wooden block about 30 cm away from the motion detector. Connect the block with a light string and weights as shown. Adjust the value of M such that the wooden block is accelerated fast enough. Adjust the height h of the block M is 20 cm from the ground. The wooden block stops accelerating when the mass, M, hits the ground as it acquires a maximum velocity. The block will be decelerated because of the kinetic frictional forces. Make sure that the wooden block moves directly away from the motion detector as far as possible. Start the motion detector and measure the displacement as a function of time. From the data collected, calculate the deceleration of the wooden block as a function of time. Choose an appropriate region on the graph where the deceleration is approximately constant and find the average value of the deceleration. Measure the mass of the wooden block m. Calculate the experimental average value of μ_k and compare it with the expected value from *Table 7.6*. Enter data in *Table 7.6*.

Table 7.6: Determination of the value of μ_k using a motion detector

Run #	Mass of the wooden block m (kg)	Normal force = mg (N)	Measured deceleration a (m/s²)	Kinetic frictional force = ma (N)	Coefficient of kinetic friction $\mu_k = (a/g)$

Using PASCO Capstone/Datastudio Software

SET-UP

Open *DataStudio*, click on *create experiment* option. Plug the yellow wire of the motion sensor into digital channel 1, and the black wire into digital channel 2. Click *setup* button on the top left corner. Click *choose interface* button. Select *Science Workshop* 500 interface. An image will now appear in the window. Select the left most yellow highlighted port (digital channel 1). Now select the "motion sensor" sensor option. Select the "motion sensor" tab option. Set the Standard Distance to 1m. Now close the experiment setup window. Now on the top left hand corner under "data" you should have position, velocity, and acceleration folders. When you are ready to start data collection hit the "start" button.

DATA ANALYSIS

In order to graph position you need to select the graph option under the displays menu of the bottom left hand corner. Select the run you want to graph under the position heading and hit ok. Then select the appropriate region of graph and then fit the graph with the appropriate curve.

Part II
Determination of μ_k by Measuring the Acceleration of the Block Using a Motion Detector

I.   Introduction and Objectives

If you connect a block of mass m by means of a light string passing over a light pulley and attach a mass, M, the net force acting on the block will be

$$Mg - f_k$$

If $Mg > f_k$ the net force results in an acceleration of the system. If we measure the acceleration of the block using a motion detector, one can calculate the kinetic frictional force and hence the coefficient of kinetic friction.

II.   Materials

Wooden block, light pulley, light inextensible string, motion detector

III. Theory

The net force acting on the system = $(Mg - f_k)$

The acceleration experienced by the block

$$a = \frac{Mg - \mu_k m_1 g}{M + m_1}$$

The coefficient of kinetic friction (μ_k) can be written as

$$\mu_k = \frac{Mg - a(M + m_1)}{m_1 g} \tag{7.5}$$

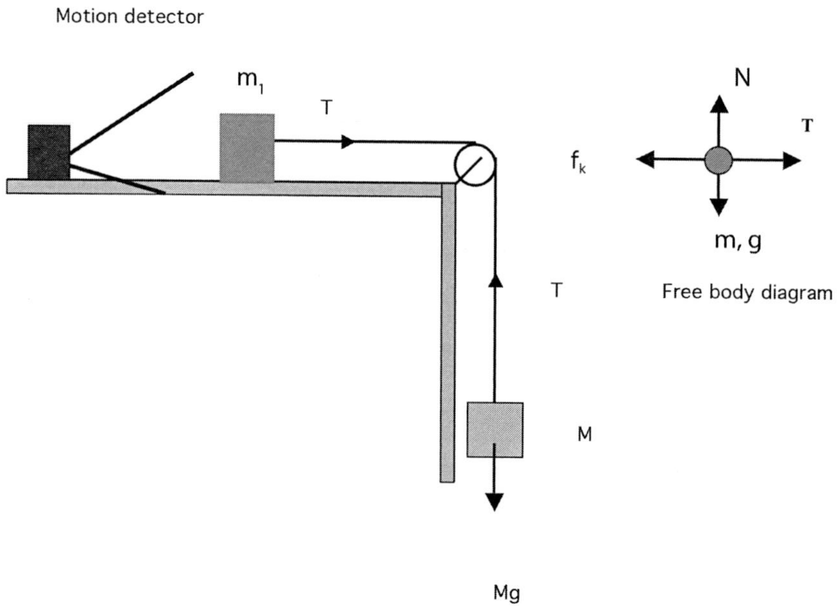

Figure 7.6: Experimental arrangement for determining the coefficient of kinetic friction by measuring the acceleration of the block using a motion detector.

IV. Experimental

In this experiment, you will fix a light pulley at the edge of a table as shown in Fig. 7.6. Connect a wooden block by means of an inextensible string and light pulley to a weight hanger suspended at the edge of the table. Hold the wooden block by hand and add weights to the hanger. You will keep sufficient weights on the hanger such that when you release the wooden block, it accelerates. You will measure the acceleration of the block using a motion detector and calculate the acceleration due to gravity, *g*.

Hold mass m_1 by your hand, add appropriate weights to the hanger and release it. Start the motion detector, measure the displacement vs. time, and calculate the velocity vs. time and acceleration vs. time using the built-in software. Repeat the measurements for different values of *M*. Enter the data in *Table 7.7*.

Table 7.7: Determination of the value of μ_k using a motion detector

Run #	m_1 (kg)	M (kg)	Mg (N)	Measured a (m/s²)	Coefficient of kinetic friction $\mu_k = (Mg - a(M + m_1))/m_1 g$

V. Questions

1. Do your experimental data support that in general $\mu_s > \mu_K$. Give logical reasons why you would expect $\mu_s > \mu_K$.

2. Can you cite a couple of examples from our daily experiences where we notice that $\mu_s > \mu_k$?

3. It is stated that the frictional force depends on the normal force. From the experimental data you collected, can you draw this conclusion? Give details.

4. Experimentally observed qualitative features of the frictional forces are given in the text Section 7, page 118. Give your explanations as why each of them seem to be logical, or perhaps not, from your perspective?

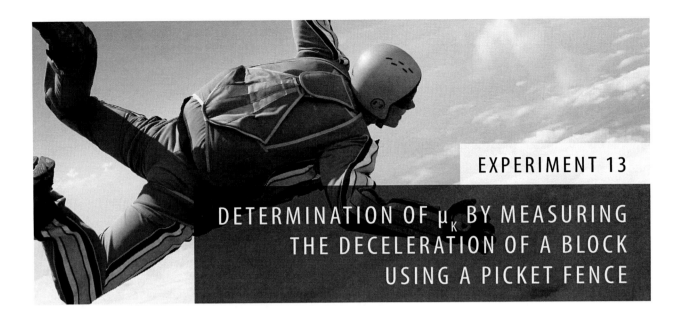

I.   Introduction and Objectives

The experimental arrangement is shown in Fig. 7.7. Using putty, fix the picket fence to the wooden block as shown. Keep a photo-gate at some distance from the wooden block (about 10 cm away). When you release the wooden block and leave it, make sure that the picket fence passes through the photo-gate. The wooden block will be experiencing deceleration because of frictional forces. If you measure the deceleration, knowing the mass of the block, you can calculate the kinetic frictional force and hence the coefficient of kinetic friction. The principle of the experiment is the same as in Experiment 12. The main difference is that you will use the picket fence instead of the motion detector to measure the deceleration.

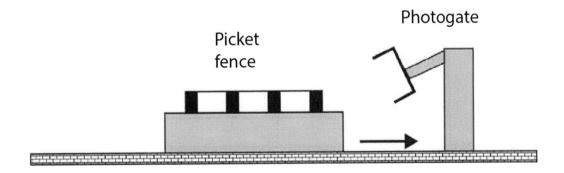

Figure 7.7: Experimental setup for measuring the coefficient of kinetic friction using a picket fence.

OBJECTIVE

To determine the coefficient of kinetic friction by measuring the deceleration of a block moving on a table using a picket fence.

II.   Equipment

Photo-gate sensor, picket fence, wooden block, PC

III.   Theory

Consider a block of mass m moving on a table. Because of frictional forces, the block would experience constant deceleration. Using a picket fence arrangement, one can measure the displacement of the block as a function of time and obtain the value of this deceleration. Knowing the deceleration, one can calculate the kinetic frictional force and the coefficient of kinetic friction.

Using PASCO Capstone/Datastudio Software

SET-UP

Open *DataStudio*, click on *create experiment* option. Plug the photo-gate into digital channel 1. Click *setup* button on the top left corner. Click *choose interface* button. Select *Science Workshop* 500 interface. An image will now appear in the window. Select the left most yellow highlighted port (digital channel 1). Now select the "Photo-gate and Picket Fence" sensor option. Select the "Constants" tab and set your band spacing. Now close the experiment setup window. Now on the top left hand corner under "data" you should have position, velocity, and acceleration folders. When you are ready to start data collection hit the "start" button. After you are done collecting data, hit the "stop" button.

DATA ANALYSIS

To graph the position, velocity, or acceleration, select the graph option in the display menu. Chose the run you want to graph under the appropriate parameter folder and hit ok. Then choose the correct fit for the data.

IV.   Experimental

Keep the wooden block about 30 cm away from the motion detector. Connect the block with a light string and weights as shown in Fig. 7.8. Adjust the value of M such that the wooden block is accelerated fast enough. Adjust the height h of the block M is 20 cm from the ground. The wooden block stops accelerating when the mass, M, hits the ground as it acquires a maximum velocity. The block will be decelerated because of the kinetic frictional forces. Make sure that the wooden block and the picket fence moves towards the photogate as far as possible. Using the picket fence software, measure the deceleration a experienced by the block. Measure the mass of the wooden block m. Calculate the experimental average value of μ_k and compare it with the expected value. Enter data in *Table 7.8.*

Table 7.8: Determination of the value of μ_k using a picket fence.

Run #	Mass of the wooden block + picket fence m (kg)	Normal force = mg (N)	Measured deceleration a (m/s²)	Kinetic frictional force = ma (N)	Coefficient of kinetic friction $\mu_k = (a/g)$

Part II
Determination of the Value of μ_k by Measuring the Acceleration of the Block Using Picket Fence

I.   Introduction and Objectives

In this experiment, you will fix a light pulley at the edge of a table as shown in Fig. 7.8. Connect a wooden block by means of an inextensible string passing over a light pulley to a weight hanger suspended at the edge of the table. You will hold the wooden block and place sufficient weights on the hanger such that when you release the wooden block, it moves with acceleration. You will measure the acceleration of the block using a picket fence and calculate the coefficient of kinetic friction.

OBJECTIVES

To measure the coefficient of kinetic friction by measuring the acceleration of a block using a picket fence.

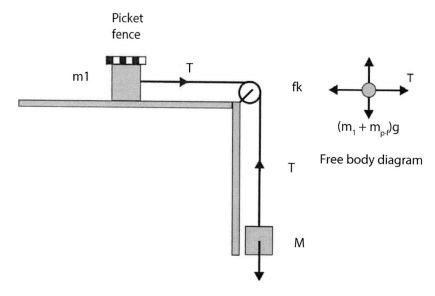

Figure 7.8: Experimental arrangement for determining the coefficient of kinetic friction by measuring the acceleration of the block using a picket fence.

II. Materials

Wooden block, picket fence, light pulley, weight hanger, weights, PC

III. Theory

The net force acting on the system $= (Mg - f_k)$

The acceleration experienced by the block

$$a = \frac{Mg - \mu_k m_1 g}{M + m_1}$$

The coefficient of kinetic friction (μ_k) can be written as

$$\mu_k = \frac{Mg - a(M + m_1)}{m_1 g} \qquad (7.5)$$

Here, m_1 is the mass of the block m_1 plus the picket fence plus the putty you used to fix the picket fence to the block m_1.

IV. Experimental

Hold mass m_1 by your hand and add sufficient weights to the hanger such that the block moves with acceleration when you release the block. Release the block and measure the acceleration a using the picket fence software. Repeat the measurements for different values of M. Enter data in *Table 7.9*.

Table 7.9: Determination of the value of μ_k using a picket fence

Run #	m_1 (kg)	M (kg)	Mg (N)	Measured acceleration a (m/s^2)	Coefficient of kinetic friction $\mu_k = (Mg - a(M + m_1))/m_1 g$

V. Questions

1. Do your experimental data support that in general $\mu_s > \mu_K$. Give logical reasons why you would expect $\mu_s > \mu_K$.

2. Can you cite a couple of examples from our daily experiences where we notice that $\mu_s > \mu_K$?

3. It is stated that the frictional force depends on the normal force. From the experimental data you collected, can you draw this conclusion? Give details.

4. Experimentally observed qualitative features of the frictional forces are given in the text, in Section 7. Give your explanations as why each of them seem to be logical, or perhaps not, from your perspective?

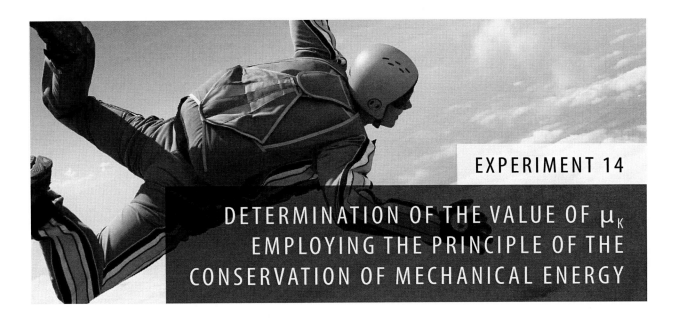

DETERMINATION OF THE VALUE OF μ_K EMPLOYING THE PRINCIPLE OF THE CONSERVATION OF MECHANICAL ENERGY

I. Introduction and Objectives

In this experiment, you will connect a light string to a wooden block, pass it over a light pulley at the edge of the table, and then connect it to a weight hanger. The external forces acting on the system are the gravitational force, Mg, and the frictional force, f_k. If you let the weights fall through a height, d, the potential energy lost by the system is equal to the kinetic energy gained by the system plus the work done in overcoming the frictional force. Knowing the change in the potential energy and the kinetic energy gained, one can calculate the work done to overcome the frictional force. Knowing the frictional force, one can calculate the coefficient of kinetic friction.

OBJECTIVES

To determine the coefficient of kinetic friction between a wooden block and a table using the principle of conservation of energy.

II. Materials

Wooden block, photo-gate sensor, light pulley, weight hanger, weights, sensor flag to measure the velocity, PC

III. Theory

The experimental arrangement is shown in Fig. 7.9. Fix a flag on a wooden block with putty. Fix the photo-gate as shown and run the software for velocity measurement. Put the wooden block at the center of the table such that the block can traverse a distance of about 50-cm without hitting the end of the table. Release the wooden block a couple of times and check whether the flag passes through the photo-gate without interruption. Also check that mass M does not hit the ground before the flag passes through the photo-gate. The free body diagram of the wooden block gives the details of the forces acting on it.

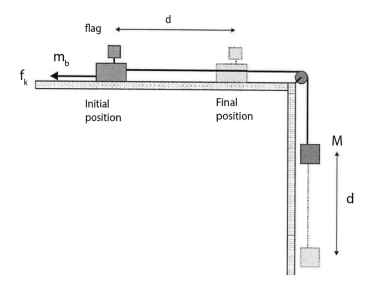

Figure 7.9: Experimental arrangement for the determination of the coefficient of kinetic friction employing the principle of conservation of mechanical energy.

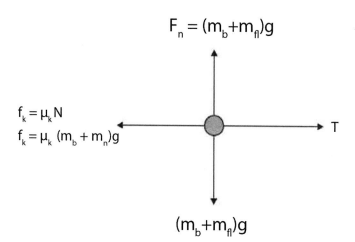

Figure 7.10: Free-body diagram of $(m_b + m_{fl})$.

Hold mass m_b at the initial position. Release the block gently and let it pass through the photo-gate without interruption. Conservation of energy gives

$$Mgd = \mu_k (m_b + m_{fl})gd + \frac{1}{2}(m_b + m_{fl})v^2 + \frac{1}{2}Mv^2$$

Here, v is the velocity when the block has moved a distance d. The final velocity is measured by the photogate. Since the block is released from rest, the initial velocity of the block is zero. In the above equation, since you used a light, inextensible string, the distance traveled by M is equal to the distance traveled by $(m_b + m_{fl})$.

$$Mgd = \mu_k (m_b + m_{fl})gd + \frac{1}{2}(m_b + m_{fl})v^2 + \frac{1}{2}Mv^2$$

$$\mu_k = (Mgd - \frac{1}{2}(m_b + m_{fl})v^2 - \frac{1}{2}Mv^2) / ((m_b + m_{fl})gd)$$

$$\mu_k = \frac{Mgd - (1/2)(m_b + m_{fl})v^2 - (1/2)Mv^2}{(m_b + m_{fl})gd} \tag{7.6}$$

Using PASCO Capstone/Datastudio Software

SET-UP

Open *DataStudio*, click on *create experiment* option. Attach the photo-gate to the projectile launcher, and then plug the photo-gate into digital channel 1. Next plug the receptor panel to channel 2. Click *setup* button on the top left corner. Click the *Choose Interface* button. Select *Science Workshop* 500 interface. An image will now appear in the window. Select the left most yellow highlighted port (digital channel 1). Now select the "photo-gate" sensor option. Select the "constants" tab and put in the flag length. Now close the experiment setup window. Now on the top left hand corner under "data" you should have a "velocity" folder. When you are ready to start data collection hit the "start" button.

DATA ANALYSIS

In order to the velocity you need to select the graph option under the displays menu of the bottom left hand corner. Select whichever run you want to measure under velocity folder and hit ok. You should see a point, which will represent the velocity.

Table 7.10: Determination of the coefficient of kinetic friction using conservation of energy

Run #	m_b (kg)	m_n (kg)	v (m/s)	d (m)	$(m_b + m_{fl})$ (kg)	M (kg)	Coefficient of kinetic friction from (Eq: 7.6) μ_K	Accepted value (from Table) of μ_K

Distance traveled by the block (m) =

Acceleration due to gravity = 9.81 m/s²

Percent error =

CALCULATIONS

All the calculations must be done using the Excel software and Excel worksheets should be submitted along with the lab report.

IV.   Questions

1.   Do your experimental data support that in general $\mu_s > \mu_K$. Give logical reasons why you would expect $\mu_s > \mu_K$.

2.   Can you cite a couple of examples from our daily experiences where we notice that $\mu_s > \mu_K$?

3.   It is stated that the frictional force depends on the normal force. From the experimental data you collected, can you draw this conclusion? Give details.

4.   Experimentally observed qualitative features of the frictional forces are given in the text, Section 7. Give your explanations as why each of them seem to be logical, or perhaps not, from your perspective?

EXPERIMENT 15

TERMINAL VELOCITY

I.   Introduction and Objectives

An object moving through any medium experiences a resistive force which is often called drag force. In this experiment, you will investigate the nature of the drag force.

The drag force is a result of the numerous collisions an object experiences with the molecules of the medium as it moves in the medium. As one would expect, the drag force depends on the shape and the surface texture of the object as well as the nature of the medium in which it is moving.

If the object is not too large, and if it is moving at low enough speeds through a fluid, the drag force is proportional to the speed of the object. This is valid for the laminar flow of a liquid. Thus, the drag force

$$F_{drag} \, \alpha \, v$$

If the object is moving through a medium such as air, the medium will have turbulent flow. When the medium has a turbulent flow, the drag force is proportional to the square of the speed (v^2) of the object. The drag force is also proportional to the density of the medium (ρ) and the cross sectional area of the object (A). The drag force in a medium having turbulent flow is given by:

$$F_{drag} = \frac{1}{2}C\rho Av^2 \qquad\qquad (7.7)$$

Here, C is the drag coefficient (which depends on the shape of the object), the speed of the object and the surface texture of the object. The values of C vary from 0.4 to 2. For ordinary speeds, C is approximately constant. Equation (7.7), though valid for ordinary objects such as a ball, a sky diver, a falling water drop, or a moving car, fails for streamlined objects such as an arrow or an airplane.

Experiment 15 | Terminal Velocity   141

If you drop an object from a height, h, the initial velocity is zero and so is the drag force. As the object accelerates, the speed of the object increases with time. For low speeds, the drag force is small and can be neglected. As the object gains speed, the drag force becomes significant. If the height from which the object is dropped is sufficiently large, a condition will be reached that at a certain speed, the drag force, F_d, will be equal in magnitude but opposite in direction to the gravitational force, mg. When this condition is satisfied, the net force acting on the object is zero and therefore the acceleration of the object will also be equal to zero. The object will move with a constant speed; this is known as terminal velocity. For a turbulent medium, the condition for terminal velocity is

$$\frac{1}{2}C\rho A v_t^2 = mg \qquad (7.8)$$
$$v_t = \sqrt{\frac{2mg}{C\rho A}}$$

The magnitude of the terminal velocity is proportional to the square root of the gravitational force $(mg)^{1/2}$ and inversely proportional to $\sqrt{A}$. As the cross sectional area of the object A increases, the terminal velocity decreases.

OBJECTIVE

Measure the terminal velocity v_t, and investigate its dependence on the mass of the object.

II. Equipment

Lab interface, Logger pro, motion detector, 7 basket - type coffee filters

III. Theory

You will investigate the terminal velocity of a basket-type coffee filter as a function of the mass of the object m, and also as a function of the cross-sectional area, A of the object. For ordinary objects, terminal velocities will be reached after falling through considerable heights. Terminal speeds of some objects in free fall and the distance in meters needed to reach 95% of the terminal speed are given in *Table 7.11*.

Table 7.11: Terminal speeds of some objects in air.

Object	Terminal velocity (m/s)	Approximate height of free fall (m)
Sky diver	60	430
Basket ball	20	47
Rain drop	7	6
Parachute with a person	5	3

For this experiment, one would like to choose an object that would reach terminal velocity when it falls through the height of the room. For this reason, we have to select objects which have low mass and have large surface areas with approximately circular cross sections. Ordinary coffee filters serve this purpose reasonably well.

Using PASCO Capstone/Datastudio Software

SET-UP

Open *DataStudio*, click on *create experiment* option. Plug the yellow wire of the motion sensor into digital channel 1, and the black wire into digital channel 2. Click the *Setup* button on the top left corner. Click *Choose interface* button. Select *Science Workshop* 500 interface. An image will now appear in the window. Select the left most yellow highlighted port (digital channel 1). Now select the "motion sensor" sensor option. Select the "motion sensor" tab option. Set the Standard Distance to 1m. Now close the experiment setup window. Now on the top left hand corner under "data" you should have position, velocity, and acceleration folders. When you are ready to start data collection hit the "start" button.

DATA ANALYSIS

In order to graph position, velocity, and acceleration you need to select the graph option under the displays menu of the bottom left hand corner. Select the run you want to graph under the parameter heading you want and hit ok. Then fit the graph with an appropriate curve.

IV. Experimental Details

1. Connect the motion detector to Port 2 of the lab interface.

2. Keep the motion detector on the floor level with the motion detector facing up.

3. Hold the coffee filter as high as possible from the motion detector, start data acquisition and then release the coffee filter.

4. Plot displacement versus time, velocity versus time, acceleration versus time

5. Repeat the procedure for two, three, …seven filters and collect the data.

The region on the plots that corresponds to the motion of the filters with the terminal velocity can be identified from:

1. the displacement vs. time plot where the displacement is linear with time

2. the velocity vs. time plot where the velocity is approximately constant

3. the acceleration vs. time plot where the acceleration is approximately zero.

Identify that region and read the corresponding velocity from the velocity vs. time plot. Highlight the region of interest and do statistical analysis to get the mean, max, and min values. Take the average value for your calculations and plots. Enter the data in *Table 7.12*.

Table 7.12: Terminal speeds of coffee filters in free fall.

Run #	# of filters	mass of filters (m) (kg)	Terminal speed (v_t) (m/s)	Initial position of filter/s y (m)	Final position of filter/s y' (m)	height of free fall $y - y' = h$ (m)	($\sqrt{mg}$)

Transfer the data to an Excel worksheet and plot v_t versus $\sqrt{mg}$. An approximate straight line shows that the terminal velocity is proportional to $\sqrt{mg}$ establishing the relationship given by (Eq: 7.9).

V.   Questions

1. As discussed in the text, the drag force in liquids with laminar flow will be proportional to mg whereas in air with turbulent flow, it will be proportional to $\sqrt{mg}$. For the free fall of the coffee filters you studied, which model does your data support?

   (Plot v_t vs. mg and v_t vs. $\sqrt{mg}$. Fit the data to an equation of a straight line. From the quality of the fits and the R^2 values of the fits, you will be able to infer whether v^t is linear with mg or $\sqrt{mg}$.)

2. Suppose that you have measured the terminal velocity $v_{t,4}$ for say 4 filters. What would be your best estimate for the terminal velocity $v_{t,9}$ for 9 filters in terms of $v_{t,4}$?

3. If $h_{t,9}$ corresponds to the height through which 9 filters have to free fall to reach the terminal velocity, what would be the corresponding height $h_{t,16}$ for 16 filters to reach the terminal velocity corresponding to $v_{t,16}$?

REFERENCES

1. C. Brueningsen et al, Modeling *Air Drag*, Physics Teacher Vol. 32, Oct. 1994, p 439.

2. V. Pagonis et al, *Effects of Air Resistance*, Physics Teacher Vol. 35, Sept. 1997, p 364.

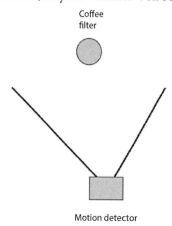

Figure 7.11: Experimental arrangement for measuring the terminal velocity of a coffee filter.

Conservation of Mechanical Energy

Experiments 16 & 17

CONSERVATION OF MECHANICAL ENERGY OF A BALL LAUNCHED VERTICALLY UPWARDS

I. Introduction and Objectives

In this experiment, you will investigate the principle of conservation of mechanical energy. The sum of the kinetic and potential energies of a body is defined as its mechanical energy. If the forces are conservative, the total mechanical energy of an object remains constant. The forces are said to be conservative if the object does not lose an appreciable amount of energy to other forms of energy such as heat. In this experiment, you will neglect the energy lost due to air resistance, which is small.

II. Equipment

Projectile launcher, computer, photo-gates

III. Theory

If the frictional forces are negligible, the mechanical energy of an object is conserved. If the frictional forces are significant, some of the mechanical energy is converted into heat and therefore, the mechanical energy is not conserved. To prove conservation of mechanical energy, we restrict ourselves to systems where the frictional losses are small. We will consider a ball launched vertically and compare its mechanical energy at the launch and when it has reached the highest point.

Conservation of Mechanical Energy

The total mechanical energy, ME, of an object is the sum of its kinetic energy, KE, and the potential energy PE at that instant

$$ME = PE + KE$$

If v_i is the initial velocity of the ball, the initial kinetic energy is:

$$KE = \frac{1}{2}mv_i^2$$

If we choose the point at which the ball is launched as the reference point for the calculation of the potential energy, the potential energy at this point is equal to zero.

The total mechanical energy at the launch $= \frac{1}{2}mv_i^2$ \hfill (8.1)

The final speed at the highest point is equal to zero. The potential energy at the highest point with respect to the point of launch is mgh, where h is the height corresponding to the highest point reached by the ball measured from the reference point (the point from which the ball was launched).

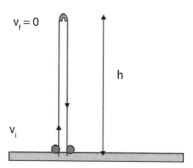

Figure 8.1: Trajectory of a ball launched vertically upwards.
For clarity, the return path of the ball is spatially displaced.

The total mechanical energy at the highest point $= mgh$ \hfill (8.2)

Measure the initial speed of the ball, v_i, using photo-gates and the maximum height, h, reached by the projectile. You will calculate the values using (Eq: 8.1) and (Eq: 8.2) and compare them.

Using Datastudio Software

SET-UP

Open *DataStudio*, click on *create experiment* option. Attach the photo-gate to the projectile launcher, then plug the photo-gate into digital channel 1. Next plug the receptor panel to channel 2. Click *setup* button on the top left corner. Click choose *interface* button. Select *Science Workshop* 500 interface. An image will now appear in the window. Select the left most yellow highlighted port (digital channel 1). Now select the "photo-gate" sensor option. Now select the digital channel 2 image and select the "photo-gate" sensor option. Now close the experiment setup window. Now on the top left hand corner under "data" you should a folder for "time between any gates" along with others. When you are ready to start data collection hit the "start" button.

DATA ANALYSIS

In order to graph velocity you need to select the graph option under the displays menu of the bottom left hand corner. Select whichever run you want to measure under the velocity folder and hit ok. You should see a point, which will represent the elapsed time.

IV. Experimental Details

Clamp the projectile launcher to the edge of a table. Point the launcher such that the ball may be launched vertically upwards. Make a couple of trial runs to ensure that for all ranges the ball does not hit the ceiling. If the ball did hit the ceiling, either work with short ranges only, or try to clamp the launcher to a table closer to the floor.

Attach a photo-gate to the bracket of the launcher and connect the photo-gate to DG1.

Open: Logger Pro, Photo-gate, Pulse Timing (In this mode, timing will begin when the photo-gate DG1 is blocked and will continue until the photo-gate DG1 is unblocked)

Measure the diameter of the ball and enter the data in the computer.

Adjust the angle of the projector to 90° and shoot the ball vertically upwards.

Measure the maximum height reached by the ball from the middle point of the photo-gate.

Alternatively, one can use two photo-gates and measure the average speed as the ball intercepts the two LED beams. Attach two photo-gates to the bracket of the launcher and connect the photo-gate nearer to the launcher to DG1 and the other to DG2.

Open: Logger Pro, Photo-gate, Pulse Timing (In this mode, timing will begin when the photo-gate DG1 is blocked and will continue until the photo-gate DG2 is blocked). Measure the distance between the photo-gates and enter the data in the computer. In this case the height will be measured from the middle point of the sensors.

Enter the data in *Table 8.1* on the following page.

V. Questions

(Submit answers to the following questions in your lab report)

1. From the data you have collected, can you conclude that the total mechanical energy is conserved? How do you explain the possible observed deviations?

2. If you have an ideal experiment (though no experiment is ideal), what value would you expect for the percentage change in the mechanical energy? If the value you obtained is different from what you expected, explain possible reasons for the observed deviations.

3. What are the sources of random errors in this experiment? How do you minimize them?

4. Can you identify possible systematic errors in this experiment and explain how you would try to minimize them.

5. In this experiment, the final velocity may be expressed in terms of the initial velocity

$$v_f^2 = v_i^2 - 2gh$$

At the highest point, $v_f = 0$, therefore

$$v_i^2 = 2gh \text{ or } h = v_i^2/2g$$

Calculate the values of h using the equation above and compare them with the corresponding measured values. If they are <u>not</u> in perfect agreement, give your explanations for the observed discrepancies.

Table 8.1: Conservation of mechanical energy of a ball launched vertically upwards.

Run #	Range of projectile	Initial velocity v_i (m/s)	Mass of the ball (kg)	Kinetic energy at launch $= (\frac{1}{2}) m v_i^2$ (J)	Maximum height reached h (m)	Potential energy at the highest point = mgh (J)	% Change in ME = $\frac{PE\text{-}KE}{KE}$ x 100
	Short						
1	Trial I						
2	Trial II						
3	Trial III						
	Medium						
4	Trial I						
5	Trail II						
6	Trial III						
	Long						
7	Trail I						
8	Trial II						
9	Trial III						

Note: Measure the height from the photogate used to measure the initial velocity and not from the floor.

EXPERIMENT 17

CONSERVATION OF MECHANICAL ENERGY USING A GLIDER AND AN AIR TRACK

I. Introduction and Objectives

In this experiment, you will investigate the principle of conservation of mechanical energy. The sum of the kinetic and potential energies of an object is defined as its mechanical energy. If the forces are conservative, the total mechanical energy of an object or a system of objects remains constant. The forces will be conservative if the object/system does not loose an appreciable amount of energy to other forms such as heat.

II. Equipment

Air track, glider, weights, photo-gates, and computer

III. Theory

Conservation of Mechanical Energy

The mechanical energy, ME, of an object/system is the sum of its kinetic energy, KE, and the potential energy PE, at that instant

$$ME = PE + KE$$

If the frictional forces are negligible, the mechanical energy of the object/system is conserved. If the frictional forces are significant, some of the mechanical energy is converted into heat, and conservation of mechanical energy will not hold. To prove conservation of mechanical energy, we restrict ourselves to such systems where the frictional losses are small.

In this experiment you will investigate whether the total mechanical energy of a system consisting of a mass coupled to a glider on an air track remains constant or not. We have chosen an air track so that the losses due to frictional forces are negligible.

As shown in Fig. 8.2, connect a glider to a weight hanger using an inextensible light string. Initially, hold the glider so that all the masses are stationary. When you release the glider, it moves horizontally over a distance, d, and the weight hanger moves by the same distance vertically. Consider the final positions shown by the dotted lines in Fig. 8.2.

The decrease in the potential energy of the system = Mgd

The increase in the kinetic energy of the system = $(½) (M + m) v^2$

The change in the mechanical energy of the system = $-Mgd + (½) (M + m) v^2$

If the total mechanical energy of the system is conserved, the change in the mechanical energy of the system will be zero.

IV.   Experimental Details

Using a level indicator, adjust the air track such that it is horizontal. Keep a glider on the air track and adjust the airflow such that the glider moves freely on the air track with no friction. You can test this condition by giving a very gentle push to the glider in the forward and backward directions of the air track. Make sure that the glider is stationary at any location on the air track when no external force is applied.

Fix the flag on the glider.

Measure the mass of the glider + flag. Let this be m.

Measure the mass of the hanger + mass of the weights added. Let this be M.

Position and adjust the photo-gate for measuring the velocity. You will employ the motion detector software. Position the photo-gate such that you will be able to measure the speed of the glider after it has traveled a distance d.

Measure the velocity of the glider using the flag and the photo-gate arrangement when it has moved a distance d from the original rest position. Energy conservation gives

$$Mgd = (1/2) mv^2 + (1/2) Mv^2 = (1/2) (m + M) v^2 \tag{8.3}$$

Using PASCO Capstone/Datastudio Software

SET-UP

Open *DataStudio*, click on *create experiment* option. Attach the photo-gate to the projectile launcher, then plug the photo-gate into digital channel 1. Next plug the receptor panel to channel 2. Click *setup* button on the top left corner. Click choose *interface* button. Select *Science Workshop* 500 interface. An image will now appear in the window. Select the left most yellow highlighted port (digital channel 1). Now select the "photo-gate" sensor option. Select the "constants" tab and put in the flag length. Now close the experiment setup window. Now on the top left hand corner under "data" you should have a "velocity" folder. When you are ready to start data collection hit the "start" button.

DATA ANALYSIS

IIn order to the velocity you need to select the graph option under the displays menu of the bottom left hand corner. Select whichever run you want to measure under velocity folder and hit ok. You should see a point, which will represent the velocity.

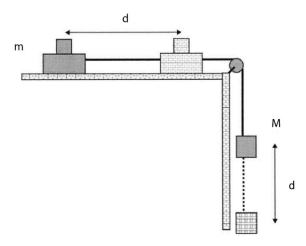

Figure 8.2: Conservation of mechanical energy using an air track.

The quantity on the left side of Eq. 8.3 gives the decrease in the potential energy of the system whereas the quantity on the right side gives the increase in the kinetic energy of the system. Enter the data in *Table 8.2*.

Table 8.2: Conservation of mechanical energy using a glider on an air track

Run #	Mass of hanger + weights M (kg)	Mass of glider + flag m (kg)	Velocity of the glider v (m/s)	d (m)	Potential energy lost Mgd (J)	KE gained $(1/2)$ $(m + M)$ v^2 (J)	% Change in ME = $\frac{PE-KE}{KE}$ x 100
1							
2							
3							
4							
5							
6							

V.   Questions

(Submit answers to the following questions in your lab report)

1. From the data you have collected, can you conclude that the total mechanical energy is conserved? How would you explain the possible observed deviations? How would you minimize the errors in this experiment?

2. Can you identify possible systematic errors in this experiment and explain how you would try to minimize them?

3. If the frictional forces on m are not negligible, and if f_k is the kinetic frictional force, modify (Eq: 8.3) to account for the frictional force.

4. If the coefficient of kinetic friction is 0.2, what fraction of the total mechanical energy is lost due to frictional forces?

Conservation of Linear Momentum

Experiments 18, 19, 20 & 21

I. Introduction

Conservation of linear momentum is one of the important fundamental laws of physics which is valid in both elastic and inelastic collisions. The propulsion of a rocket, the motion of a jet plane, and the recoil of a gun are some examples of the consequences of conservation of linear momentum. To experimentally investigate the conservation of linear momentum, we need to minimize frictional forces and therefore we will employ an air track.

II. Theory

The momentum, **p**, of an object of mass m moving with a velocity, **v**, is defined as

$$\mathbf{p} = m\mathbf{v} \tag{9.1}$$

Since the velocity, **v**, is a vector quantity so is the linear momentum, p.

Newton's second law states "Rate of change of linear momentum is equal to the net external force acting on the object"

$$\mathbf{F} = d\mathbf{p}/dt$$

If the net external force is equal to zero, then

$$\mathbf{F} = d\mathbf{p}/dt = 0$$

$$d\mathbf{p} = 0, \ \mathbf{p} \text{ is a constant.}$$

i.e., the change in the momentum is zero. Therefore, if the net external force acting on the system is equal to zero, the momentum of the system remains constant, or the linear momentum is conserved. The internal forces acting on the atoms/molecules in an object form equal and opposite pairs. The net effect of these forces on the motion of the object as a whole is equal to zero.

In any collision process, if the net external force acting on the system is equal to zero, the momentum remains constant. The forces acting on the bodies during the collision process also form equal and opposite pairs. The net effect of these forces on the motion of the system as a whole is equal to zero.

In any collision process, if $\mathbf{p}_i$ is the initial momentum of the system before the collision and $\mathbf{p}_f$ is the final momentum of the system after the collision, the change in the momentum

$$\mathbf{p}_f - \mathbf{p}_i = 0, \text{ or } \mathbf{p}_f = \mathbf{p}_i.$$

Remember, $\mathbf{p}_i$ and $\mathbf{p}_f$ are vector quantities and we have to employ the vector manipulation procedures in handling them. However, since you will be investigating the momentum conservation in one dimension only, manipulation of the vector quantities in one dimension is much simpler.

Let us consider two objects of masses m_1 and m_2 having initial velocities $\mathbf{v}_{1i}$ and $\mathbf{v}_{2i}$ and after the collision let their velocities be $\mathbf{v}_{1f}$ and $\mathbf{v}_{2f}$ respectively (Fig. 9.1). Let $\mathbf{p}_{1i}$ and $\mathbf{p}_{2i}$ be their respective initial momenta, $\mathbf{p}_{1f}$ and $\mathbf{p}_{2f}$ be their corresponding momenta after the collision.

Before collision			After collision		
Masses	m_1	m_2	Masses	m_1	m_2
Initial velocities	$\mathbf{v}_{1i}$	$\mathbf{v}_{2i}$	Final velocities	$\mathbf{v}_{1f}$	$\mathbf{v}_{2f}$
Initial momenta	$\mathbf{P}_{1i}$	$\mathbf{P}_{2i}$	Final momenta	$\mathbf{P}_{1f}$	$\mathbf{P}_{2f}$

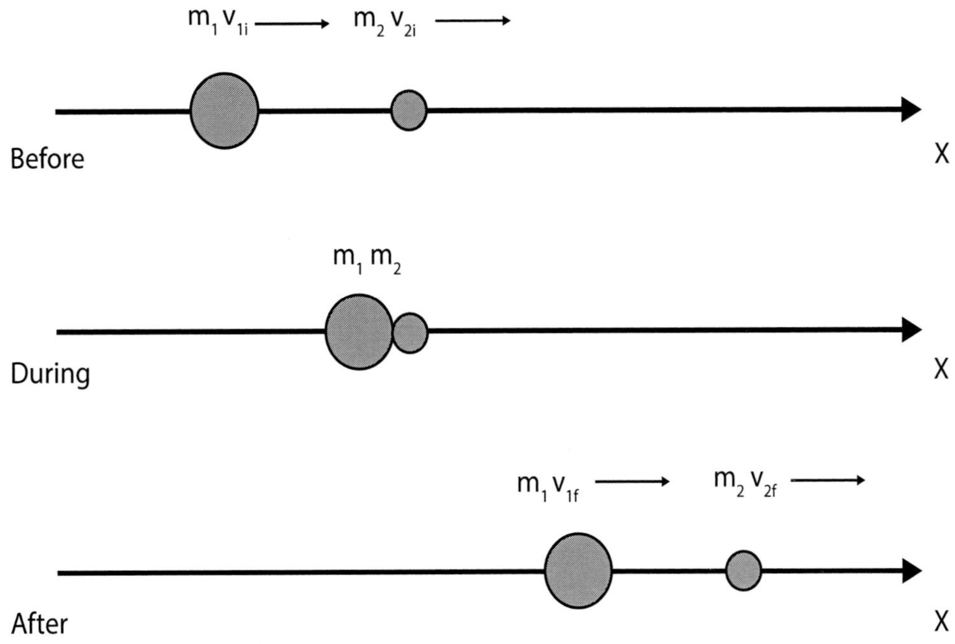

Figure 9.1: Two bodies undergoing an elastic collision in one dimension.

Conservation of momentum gives

$$\mathbf{P}_{1i} + \mathbf{P}_{2i} = \mathbf{P}_{1f} + \mathbf{P}_{2f}$$

$$m_1 \mathbf{v}_{1i} + m_2 \mathbf{v}_{2i} = m_1 \mathbf{v}_{1f} + m_2 \mathbf{v}_{2f} \tag{9.2}$$

As stated earlier, since we are investigating the motion in one dimension only, the momenta and the velocities can be manipulated employing scalar algebra.

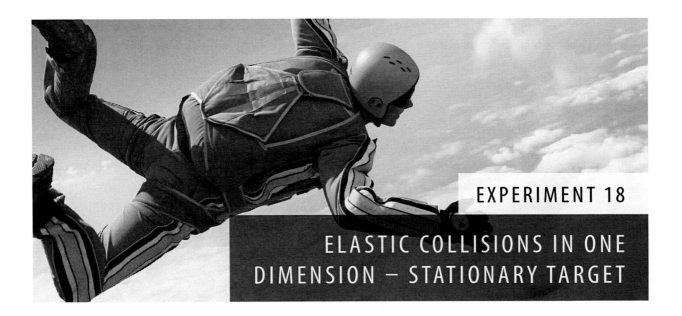

I. Objective

To verify the law of conservation of linear momentum in one dimension.

II. Experimental Details

You will use an air track, two aluminum gliders, two photo-gates, and two glider flags of ~ 25-mm length or less.

Open photo-gate timing and Collision Timing software. The timing mode uses two photo-gates DG 1 and DG 2. In this mode, each photo-gate measures the times independently and lists them in the data table under the columns Delta T1 and Delta T2. For each photo-gate the times are listed in the order in which they were measured. The times corresponding to the photo-gate #1 are separately listed from those of the photo-gate #2. This method of listing would enable you to unambiguously identify the measured velocities with the corresponding gliders.

A. Elastic Collisions in One Dimension – Stationary target

Collisions are said to be elastic if the total mechanical energy of the system before collision is equal to the total mechanical energy of the system after the collision. If the mechanical energy of the system is not conserved in a collision process, then it is called an inelastic collision. Momentum conservation is valid in both elastic and inelastic collisions.

Case 1: Elastic collision of two gliders of equal mass ($m_1 = m_2$)

The conservation of momentum gives

$$m_1 \mathbf{v}_{1i} + m_2 \mathbf{v}_{2i} = m_1 \mathbf{v}_{1f} + m_2 \mathbf{v}_{2f} \tag{9.3}$$

If m_2 is initially at rest $\mathbf{v}_{2i} = 0$

Using Datastudio Software

SET-UP

Open *DataStudio*, click on *create experiment* option. Attach the photo-gate to the projectile launcher, then plug the photo-gate into digital channel 1. Next plug the receptor panel to channel 2. Click *setup* button on the top left corner. Click *choose interface* button. Select *Science Workshop 500* interface. An image will now appear in the window. Select the left most yellow highlighted port (digital channel 1). Now select the "photo-gate" sensor option. Select the "constants" tab and put in the flag length. Now close the experiment setup window. Now on the top left hand corner under "data" you should have a "velocity" folder. When you are ready to start data collection hit the "start" button.

DATA ANALYSIS

In order to graph velocity you need to select the graph option under the displays menu of the bottom left hand corner. Select whichever run you want to measure under the velocity folder and hit ok. You should see a point, which will represent the elapsed time.

The resulting equation will be

$$m_1\mathbf{v}_{1i} = m_1\mathbf{v}_{1f} + m_2\mathbf{v}_{2f} \tag{9.4}$$

Further, since $m_1 = m_2$, (Eq. 9.4) reduces to

$$\mathbf{v}_{1i} = \mathbf{v}_{1f} + \mathbf{v}_{2f} \tag{9.5}$$

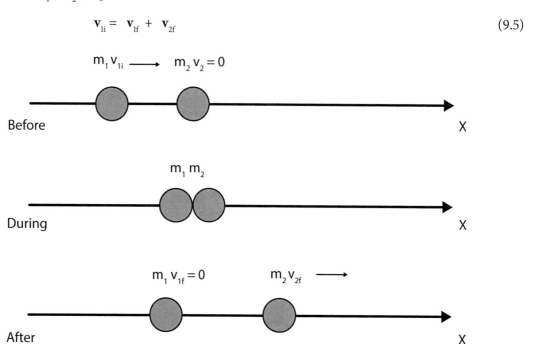

Figure 9.2 Elastic collision in one dimension – stationary target

For the investigation of elastic collisions, you will fix the rubber band attachments to the gliders. Make a choice whether you want the gliders to collide moving in opposite directions or moving in the same direction. Position the gliders appropriately so that the collision occurs on the elastic rubber band you have fixed o r on the elastic material you fixed on the gliders. First, try a couple of times by pushing t he gliders appropriately and observe the directions in which the gliders move after the collision. Position the photo-gates such that you can measure the velocities of both the gliders just before and immediately after the collision. Monitor carefully to see which photo-gate is measuring the velocity of which glider after the collision. This is important because the directions of the velocities of the gliders may change after the collision. Since we are considering one-dimensional head-on collision, the velocities are directed along one axis only and therefore can be either positive or negative. Take the velocities directed towards your right as positive and those directed towards your left as negative. There is nothing wrong if you choose the signs the other way as long as you consistently follow the same convention for the entire problem. Repeat the experiment three times and enter the data in *Table 9.1*. If the masses of t he gliders m_1 and m_2 are not equal, you will use (Eq. 9.4) instead of (Eq. 9.5) to prove the conservation of momentum.

Alternatively, if the masses of the gliders are not equal, you may add additional weights necessary so that they are equal to the nearest gram. When you add additional weights to the glider, make sure that you add the weights evenly on both sides of the glider.

Table 9.1: Conservation of linear momentum.
Elastic collisions between two gliders of equal mass. $(m_1 \sim m_2)$, $v_{2i} = 0$.

Take the velocity to the right as + (positive) and the velocity to the left as – (negative).
Give the appropriate signs while entering the data in the Table.

Run #	m_1 (kg)	m_2 (kg)	V_{1i} (m/s)	V_{2i} (m/s)	V_{1f} (m/s)	V_{2f} (m/s)	Initial momentum = $m_1 v_{1i}$ (kg.m)/s	Final momentum = $m_1 v_{1f} + m_2 v_{2f}$ (kg.m)/s
1				0				
2				0				
3				0				
4				0				
5				0				

Important Note: The velocities are vector quantities so are the momenta. The masses are scalar quantities. You have to choose an appropriate coordinate system so that you could assign appropriate signs to the velocities and momenta. Since we are dealing with one- dimensional motion only, the velocities and momenta will be either positive or negative depending on the coordinate system you have chosen. We will choose the velocities and momenta directed towards right as positive and towards left as negative. It is important that you take account of the signs of the velocity and the momentum in all the calculations.

B. Elastic collision of a light glider and a massive target glider at rest (m₁ < < m₂)

Add heavy weights on both sides of the target glider. Push the glider (m1) a couple of times and note the directions in which the gliders are moving after the collision. Position the photo-gates such that you will be able to measure the initial and final velocities of both the gliders just before and immediately after the collision. Here, $v_{2i} = 0$, so that

$$m_1 \mathbf{v}_{1i} = m_1 \mathbf{v}_{1f} + m_2 \mathbf{v}_{2f} \qquad (9.4)$$

Measure the values of m_1, m_2, v_{1i}, v_{1f}, and v_{2f} and enter the data in *Table 9.2*. Repeat the experiment for different values of v_{1i}. Remember that m_2 should be very much larger than m_1.

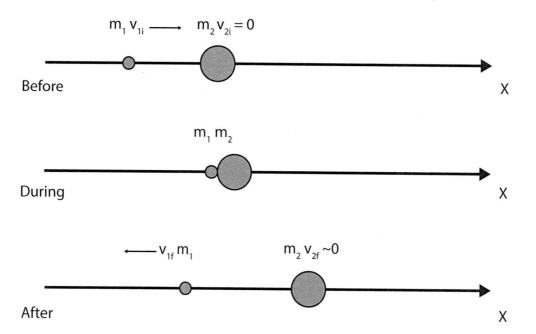

Figure 9.3: Elastic collision of a light glider and a massive glider at rest

Table 9.2: Conservation of linear momentum.

Elastic collision of a light glider and a massive target glider at rest. (m₁ << m₂), v_{2i} = 0. m₂ at rest.

Run #	m_1 (kg)	m_2 (kg)	V_{1i} (m/s)	V_{2i} (m/s)	V_{1f} (m/s)	V_{2f} (m/s)	Initial momentum = $m_1 v_{1i}$ (kg.m)/s	Final momentum = $m_1 v_{1f}$ + $m_2 v_{2f}$ (kg.m)/s
1				0				
2				0				
3				0				
4				0				
5				0				

C. Massive projectile and a light stationary target glider at rest $(m_1 \gg m_2)$, $v_{2i} = 0$. m_2 at rest

Let m_2 be initially at rest ($v_{2i} = 0$). For this condition,(Eg: 9.3) reduces to

$$m_1 \mathbf{v}_{1i} = m_1 \mathbf{v}_{1f} + m_2 \mathbf{v}_{2f} \tag{9.4}$$

Put heavy additional weights on both sides of glider 1 (m_1) and no additional weights on glider 2 (m_2). As in Case 1, study the collisions a couple of times and select appropriate positions for the two gliders and the two photo-gates. Push glider 1 so that it will have a collision with glider 2. Measure the velocities of both the gliders after the collision. Measure the masses of the gliders along with the weights. Repeat the measurements for three different values of the velocity v_{1i}. Enter the data in *Table 9.3*.

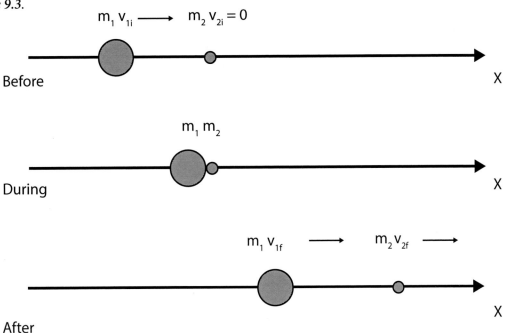

Figure 9.4: Elastic collision of a massive projectile amd a light target at rest

Table 9.3: Conservation of linear momentum.
Massive projectile and light stationary target at rest ($m_1 \ll m_2$), $v_2 = 0$. m2 at rest.

Run #	m_1 (kg)	m_2 (kg)	V_{1i} (m/s)	V_{2i} (m/s)	V_{1f} (m/s)	V_{2f} (m/s)	Initial momentum = $m_1 v_{1i}$ (kg.m)/s	Final momentum = $m_1 v_{1f} + m_2 v_{2f}$ (kg.m)/s
1				0				
2				0				
3				0				
4				0				
5				0				

III. Questions

1. (From the data you have collected for ($m_1 = m_2$), ($m_1 \ll m_2$) and ($m_1 \gg m_2$) in case (1), case (2) and case (3), can you draw some empirical conclusions concerning the final velocities of the projectile and the target? Can you give an example of each of them from your experiences in your daily life?

2. Explain how the conservation of momentum is responsible for the propulsion of a rocket.

3. In a nuclear reactor, in the fission process, neutrons are emitted at high energies. Neutrons are to be thermalized, i.e., their kinetic energies have to be significantly reduced, so that you can increase the probability for the new fission processes. You have a choice of a number of materials such as, say, heavy water, iron and lead. The neutrons experience elastic collisions with the atoms of these materials and loose their energies. Assuming the target atoms are at rest initially, out of the three materials given above which one would you prefer for efficient thermalization of neutrons? Give reasons and explanation.

4. From the data collected for inelastic collisions, is the kinetic energy conserved? (Is the kinetic energy of the gliders before the collision same as the kinetic energy of the gliders after the collision?). If not, how do you account for the loss in kinetic energy? Is this kinetic energy converted into some other form of energy? Give explanation.

EXPERIMENT 19

ELASTIC COLLISIONS - BOTH PROJECTILE AND TARGET MOVING INITIALLY

Using Datastudio Software

SET-UP

Open *DataStudio*, click on *create experiment* option. Attach the photo-gate to the projectile launcher, then plug the photo-gate into digital channel 1. Next plug the receptor panel to channel 2. Click *setup* button on the top left corner. Click *choose interface* button. Select *Science Workshop* 500 interface. An image will now appear in the window. Select the left most yellow highlighted port (digital channel 1). Now select the "photo-gate" sensor option. Now select the digital channel 2 image and select the "photo-gate" sensor option. Now close the experiment setup window. When you are ready to start data collection hit the "start" button. When the two gliders collide you must stop the data collection and hit start again. This is to ensure that you have two separate velocity runs, before and after collision.

DATA ANALYSIS

In order to graph velocity you need to select the graph option under the displays menu of the bottom left hand corner. Select whichever run you want to measure under the velocity folder and hit ok.

Case 1: Both the objects (gliders) have finite initial velocities

In this part of the experiment, you will investigate the law of conservation of momentum in elastic collisions when both the objects have finite initial velocities.

Elastic Collisions: You will attach a bumper with an elastic rubber band to one of the gliders and a bumper blade to the other glider so that the collision will be as close to an elastic one as possible. Give a gentle impulsive push to both the gliders simultaneously so that they will be moving in the opposite directions.

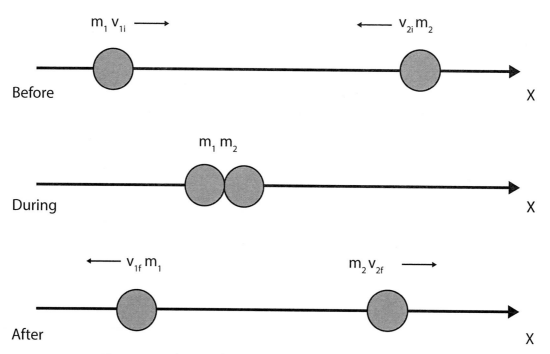

Figure 9.5 Elastic collision of two objects in one dimension –
both projectile and target moving initially.

You may also give an impulsive push in the same direction but make sure they experience collision. Undertake a couple of trials and choose appropriate initial positions of the gliders and the photo-gates so that you will be able to measure the initial and final velocities of the gliders just before and immediately after the collision. You also make a note of which photo-gate is measuring the velocity of which glider and make it certain that you identify the initial and final velocities of the gliders correctly before you enter the data in the table. Repeat the experiment for different though gentle pushes. Enter your observations in *Table 9.4*. It is important that you enter the data on velocities with proper signs. Take the velocities directed right as positive and the velocities directed left as negative.

Table 9.4: Conservation of linear momentum.
Both the objects (gliders) have finite initial velocities.

Run #	m_1 (kg)	m_2 (kg)	V_{1i} (m/s)	V_{2i} (m/s)	V_{1f} (m/s)	V_{2f} (m/s)	Initial momentum = $m_1 v_{1i} + m_2 v_{2i}$ (kg.m)/s	Final momentum = $m_1 v_{1f} + m_2 v_{2f}$ (kg.m)/s
1								
2								
3								
4								
5								

Case 2: Elastic collisions – both objects moving in the same direction

In t his experiment, you will investigate the conservation of linear momentum in elastic collisions when the two objects (gliders) are moving in the same direction. Change the positions of the bumper blade/the-elastic rubber band on the gliders such that you can investigate the elastic collision process when both the gliders are moving in the same direction. Give gentle pushes to the gliders such that they experience a collision within the length of the air track. You may have to try a couple of times to determine approximately the impulses you will give such that you can measure the initial velocities just before the collision and final velocities immediately after the collision of both the gliders. You also choose appropriate locations of the photo- gates such that you will be able to measure the corresponding velocities before and after the collision. Repeat the experiment with three different but gentle pushes and enter the data in *Table 9.5*.

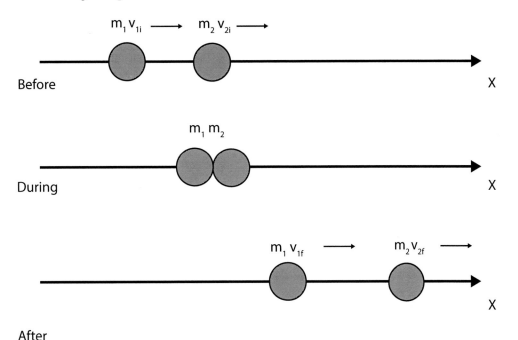

Figure 9.6 Elastic collisions. Both projectile and target moving in the same direction initially.

Table 9.5: Conservation of linear momentum.
Both the objects (gliders) moving in the same direction

Run #	m_1 (kg)	m_2 (kg)	V_{1i} (m/s)	V_{2i} (m/s)	V_{1f} (m/s)	V_{2f} (m/s)	Initial momentum = $m_1 v_{1i} + m_2 v_{2i}$ (kg.m)/s	Final momentum = $m_1 v_{1f} + m_2 v_{2f}$ (kg.m)/s
1								
2								
3								
4								
5								

Questions

1. From the data you have collected for $(m_1 = m_2)$, $(m_1 \ll m_2)$ and $(m_1 \gg m_2)$ in case (1), case (2) and case (3), can you draw some empirical conclusions concerning the final velocities of the projectile and the target? Can you give an example of each of them from your experiences in your daily life?

2. Explain how the conservation of momentum is responsible for the propulsion of a rocket.

3. In a nuclear reactor, in the fission process, neutrons are emitted at high energies. Neutrons are to be thermalized, i.e., their kinetic energies have to be significantly reduced, so that you can increase the probability for the new fission processes. You have a choice of a number of materials such as, say, heavy water, iron and lead. The neutrons experience elastic collisions with the atoms of these materials and loose their energies. Assuming the target atoms are at rest initially, out of the three materials given above which one would you prefer for efficient thermalization of neutrons? Give reasons and explanation.

4. From the data collected for inelastic collisions, is the kinetic energy conserved? (Is the kinetic energy of the gliders before the collision same as the kinetic energy of the gliders after the collision?). If not, how do you account for the loss in kinetic energy? Is this kinetic energy converted into some other form of energy? Give explanation.

EXPERIMENT 20

INELASTIC COLLISIONS USING AN AIR TRACK

Using PASCO Capstone/Datastudio Software

SET-UP

Open *DataStudio*, click on *create experiment* option. Attach the photo-gate to the projectile launcher, then plug the photo-gate into digital channel 1. Next plug the receptor panel to channel 2. Click *setup* button on the top left corner. Click *choose interface* button. Select *Science Workshop* 500 interface. An image will now appear in the window. Select the left most yellow highlighted port (digital channel 1). Now select the "photo-gate" sensor option. Now select the digital channel 2 image and select the "photo-gate" sensor option. Now close the experiment setup window. When you are ready to start data collection hit the "start" button. When the two gliders collide you must stop the data collection and hit start again. This is to ensure that you have two separate velocity runs, before and after collision.

DATA ANALYSIS

In order to graph velocity you need to select the graph option under the displays menu of the bottom left hand corner. Select whichever run you want to measure under the velocity folder and hit ok.

Inelastic Collisions-Both Projectile and Target Moving Initially

For this part of the experiment, remove the bumper with the elastic rubber band and the bumper blade from the gliders and fix blobs of sticky clay or Velcro to the gliders. You will stick the clay such that when the collision takes place, the sticky clay of both the gliders stick together and both the gliders will move with the same velocity after the collision.

Push the gliders from the ends towards the center of the table. Adjust the positions of the gliders and the photo-gates such that you will be able to measure the velocities of the gliders just before the collision and the velocity of the glider combination immediately after the collision. Repeat the experiment for three gentle impulsive pushes and enter the data in *Table 9.6*. It is important that you enter the data on velocities with proper signs. Take the velocities directed right as positive and the velocities directed left as negative.

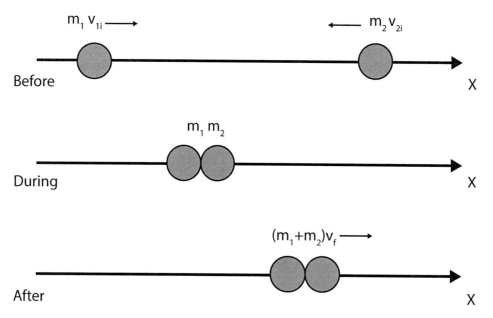

Figure 9.7 Inelastic collision. Both projectile and target moving initially.

Table 9.6: Conservation of linear momentum.
Inelastic Collisions-both projectile and target moving

Run #	m_1 (kg)	m_2 (kg)	V_{1i} (m/s)	V_{2i} (m/s)	V_f (m/s)	Initial momentum = $m_1 v_{1i} + m_2 v_{2i}$ (kg.m)/s	Final momentum = $(m_1 + m_2) v_f$ (kg.m)/s
1							
2							
3							
4							
5							

Note: You will transfer all the data to Excel spreadsheet and complete the calculations. Your report must include the worksheets from the Excel software. You are not allowed to do the calculations using a hand calculator because it is time consuming and prone to mistakes.

Questions

1. From the data collected for inelastic collisions, is the kinetic energy conserved? (Is the kinetic energy of the gliders before the collision equal to the kinetic energy of the gliders after the collision?). If not, how do you account for the loss in kinetic energy? Is this kinetic energy converted into other form of energy? Give explanation.

2. In the design of a hydroelectric power plant, you wish to have maximum impulse transferred to the turbine blade. As the water from a reservoir at an elevated level falls on the blade, the following designs for the blades are possible: (a) water splashes on the blades and the final velocity of the water is approximately equal to zero, (b) you shape the blades such that the water reverses its velocity after the impact with the blades. To achieve maximum momentum transfer to the turbine, which of the above designs would you employ? Give reasons.

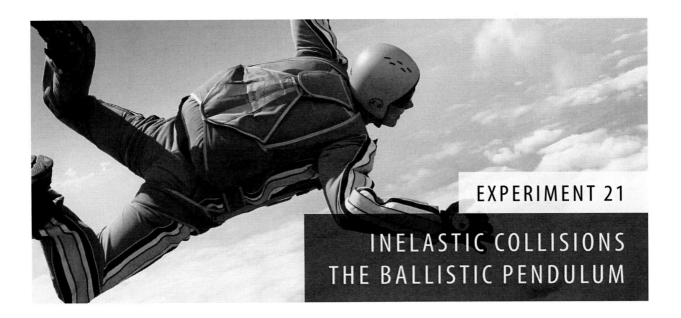

EXPERIMENT 21

INELASTIC COLLISIONS
THE BALLISTIC PENDULUM

I.   Introduction

We often hear about collisions- billiard balls collide, there is a collision of cars on the freeway, two football players collide head-on etc. In a collision process, two or more objects interact intensely for a short period of time. For example, when you hit a tennis ball with a racquet, the interaction times are of the order of a few milliseconds (10^{-3} s).

The collision is said to be elastic if the total kinetic energy of the objects before the collision is equal t o the total kinetic energy of the objects after the collision. In an inelastic collision, the total kinetic energy of the objects after the collision will not be the same as before. In an inelastic collision process, some of the kinetic energy is converted into other forms of energy such as heat. While the collision between billiard balls is an example of an elastic collision, a bullet piercing into a suspended wooden block, which is known as ballistic pendulum, is an example of an inelastic collision. In this experiment, you will investigate the inelastic collision between a ball released by a spring launcher and a suspended catcher system where it is brought to rest.

II.   Theory

Let m be the mass of the ball and v be its muzzle speed when it is launched. The launcher is adjusted to be horizontal and we would assume that its velocity is horizontal and its vertical component of the velocity is equal to zero. Let M be the mass of the catcher. Conservation of linear momentum gives

$$mv = (m + M)\,V \tag{9.6}$$

where V is the velocity of the catcher plus the ball immediately after the collision. You can obtain the value of V by measuring its instantaneous velocity immediately after the collision by means of a photo-gate. You can also obtain the value of V by measuring the height h through which the catcher is displaced after the collision.

The kinetic energy of the catcher plus ball immediately after the collision

$$KE = \frac{1}{2}(m + M)V^2$$

Because of this kinetic energy, the catcher and the ball system rises through a vertical distance h such that the potential energy gained is equal to the kinetic energy lost

$$\frac{1}{2}(m + M)V^2 = (m + M)gh$$

Using PASCO Capstone/Datastudio Software

SET-UP

Open *DataStudio*, click on *create experiment* option. Attach the photo-gate to the projectile launcher, then plug the photo-gate into digital channel 1. Next plug the receptor panel to channel 2. Click *setup* button on the top left corner. Click *choose interface* button. Select *Science Workshop* 500 interface. An image will now appear in the window. Select the left most yellow highlighted port (digital channel 1). Now select the "photo-gate" sensor option. Now select the digital channel 2 image and select the "photo-gate" sensor option. Now close the experiment setup window. When you are ready to start data collection hit the "start" button.

DATA ANALYSIS

In order to graph the corresponding velocities click on the graph option under the display menu of the bottom left hand corner. Select corresponding run and parameter folder.

III. Experimental

Clamp the projectile launcher to the end of a table. Adjust the angle of projection to zero so that the ball will be launched horizontally. Attach a photo-gate to the launcher to measure the muzzle velocity of the ball.

Align the launcher and the catcher so that the ball from the launcher enters the catcher directly. You may have to do a couple of trial runs to achieve this condition.

Using an appropriate stand, fix a meter stick vertically just behind the catcher. Hold a sheet of light cardboard just above the catcher and move the cardboard up as the catcher moves up after the collision. Note the highest position reached by the catcher. Alternately, you may use a motion detector to measure the height, *h* with a better precision.

One can also measure the velocity, *V*, of the ball plus the catcher system after the collision by fixing a flag to the catcher and measuring the transit time using a photo-gate.

Using a scale find the mass of the ball, *m*, and the mass of the catcher, *M*. Enter data in Tables 9.7-9.9.

Table 9.7: Conservation of linear momentum in one dimension-Ballistic Pendulum

Run #	Initial velocity of the ball v (m/s)	Velocity of the catcher + ball after collision V (m/s)	Mass of the ball m(kg)	Mass of the catcher M(kg)	Initial momentum mv (kg-m/s)	Final momentum $(m + M) V$ (kg-m/s)

Table 9.8: Fractional kinetic energy lost in inelastic collisions

Run #	Initial velocity of the ball v (m/s)	Velocity of the catcher + ball after collision V (m/s)	Mass of the ball m(kg)	Mass of the catcher M(kg)	Initial kinetic energy $(1/2)\,mv^2$ (J)	Final kinetic energy catcher + ball after collision $(1/2)(m+M)V^2$ (J)	Experimental ratio of $\dfrac{KE_{final}}{KE_{initial}}$	Expected ratio $\dfrac{m}{m+M}$

Table 9.9: Conservation of linear momentum in one dimension-Ballistic Pendulum

Run #	Initial velocity of the ball v (m/s)	Mass of the ball m(kg)	Initial kinetic energy $(1/2)\,mv^2$(J)	Mass of the catcher M(kg)	Initial position of the catcher assembly y (m)	Final position of the catcher assembly y' (m)	Change in the height $h =$ $(y' - y)$ (m)	Increase in the potential energy $(M + m)\,gh$ (J)	Experimental ratio of $\dfrac{KE_{final}}{KE_{initial}}$	Expected ratio $\dfrac{m}{m+M}$

IV. Questions

1. From your data and analysis

   (a) Is the linear momentum conserved? What is the percent accuracy?

   $$\% \ Accuracy = \frac{Final \ Momentum \text{ - } Initial \ momentum}{Initial \ Momentum} \ x \ 100$$

2. Is the kinetic energy conserved? Calculate the percent of the kinetic energy lost during the inelastic collision process.

3. Try to give reasons from a physical point of view why kinetic energy is not conserved in inelastic collisions? What happens to the lost kinetic energy?

4. For an inelastic collision process, show that the fractional kinetic energy lost is equal to $m/(m + M)$, where m is the mass of the projectile having an initial velocity of v and the target of mass M is initially at rest.

Elastic and Inelastic Collisions in One Dimension

Experiment 22

I.   Introduction and Objectives

A collision is said to occur when two objects impact for a relatively short period of time resulting in strong action-reaction forces on the objects. Hitting a baseball with a bat, striking a nail with a hammer, collisions between billiard balls, kicking a football, and automobile accidents are typical examples of collisions. When you hit a tennis ball with a racquet, you apply a large amount of force for a short duration of time resulting in a large change in the momentum of the ball. A good deal of information on sub-atomic particles— electrons, protons, neutrons and elementary particles— was obtained by studying collisions between them. In this experiment, you will investigate the physical laws that govern the collision processes.

II.   Theory

Collisions are generally categorized as elastic or inelastic collisions. In **elastic collisions**, the kinetic energy is conserved, i.e. the kinetic energy of the system before collision is equal to the kinetic energy of the system after collision. In **inelastic collisions**, the kinetic energy of the system is not conserved because part of the energy is lost to frictional and/or resistive components, which is converted to other forms such as thermal energy. You should note, however, that the momentum conservation is valid in both elastic and inelastic collisions. We will investigate the collision processes in one dimension using an air track. Further, for the sake of simplicity, we will focus on head-on collisions of two bodies.

Let us consider the head-on collision of two objects of masses m_1 and m_2 in one dimension (Fig. 10.1). For the sake of simplicity, let us assume that projectile m_1 is moving with an initial velocity $\mathbf{v}_{1i}$ and the target, m_2, is moving with an initial velocity, $\mathbf{v}_{2i}$. After the collision, let the velocity of m_1 be $\mathbf{v}_{1f}$ and that of m_2 be $\mathbf{v}_{2f}$. Let p_{1i} and p_{2i} be the initial momenta and p_{1f} and p_{2f} be the final momenta of m_1 and m_2 respectively.

Before collision	Projectile	Target	After Collision		
Masses	m_1	m_2	Masses	m_1	m_2
Initial velocities	$\mathbf{v}_{1i}$	$\mathbf{v}_{2i}$	Final velocities	$\mathbf{v}_{1f}$	$\mathbf{v}_{2f}$
Initial momenta	$\mathbf{p}_{1i}$	$\mathbf{p}_{2i}$	Final momenta	$\mathbf{p}_{1f}$	$\mathbf{p}_{2f}$

Conservation of linear momentum: In any collision process both elastic and inelastic, the linear momentum is conserved- i.e., the momentum of the system before the collision is equal to the momentum of the system after the collision. Conservation of momentum yields

$$\mathbf{p}_{1i} + \mathbf{p}_{2i} = \mathbf{p}_{1f} + \mathbf{p}_{2f}$$

$$m_1 \mathbf{v}_{1i} + m_2 \mathbf{v}_{2i} = m_1 \mathbf{v}_{1f} + m_2 \mathbf{v}_{2f} \tag{10.1}$$

Conservation of kinetic energy gives

$$(\tfrac{1}{2})m_1 \mathbf{v}_{1i}^2 + (\tfrac{1}{2})m_2 \mathbf{v}_{2i}^2 = (\tfrac{1}{2})m_1 \mathbf{v}_{1f}^2 + (\tfrac{1}{2})m_2 \mathbf{v}_{2f}^2 \tag{10.2}$$

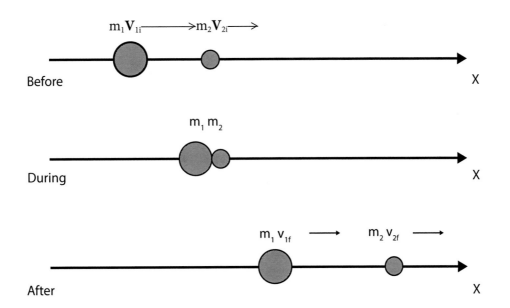

Figure 10.1: Elastic head-on collision of two bodies, projectile m_1 and target m_2.

Let us assume that the projectile is initially moving along the x-axis. Since we are investigating the head-on collision in one dimension, the vector quantities (velocity, and momentum) have only x-coordinates and can be manipulated employing the scalar algebra. (Eqs: 10.1and 10.2) may be written in scalar form

$$m_1 \mathbf{v}_{1i} + m_2 \mathbf{v}_{2i} = m_1 \mathbf{v}_{1f} + m_2 \mathbf{v}_{2f} \tag{10.3}$$

$$(\tfrac{1}{2}) \, m_1 \mathbf{v}^2_{2i} + (\tfrac{1}{2}) \, m_2 \mathbf{v}^2_{2i} = (\tfrac{1}{2}) \, m_1 \mathbf{v}^2_{1f} + (\tfrac{1}{2}) \, m_2 \mathbf{v}^2_{2f} \tag{10.4}$$

If we consider the case where the initial velocity of the target, m_2 is zero ($v_{2i} = 0$), (Eqs: 10.3 and 10.4) reduce to

$$m_1 \mathbf{v}_{1i} = m_1 \mathbf{v}_{1f} + m_2 \mathbf{v}_{2f} \tag{10.5}$$

$$m_1 \mathbf{v}^2_{1i} = m_1 \mathbf{v}^2_{1f} + m_2 \mathbf{v}^2_{2f} \tag{10.6}$$

Eq: 10.5 may be written in the form

$$m_2 \mathbf{v}_{2f} = m_1 \left(\mathbf{v}_{1i} - \mathbf{v}_{1f} \right) \tag{10.7}$$

Multiplying both sides of Eq: 10.7 by $\mathbf{v}_{2f}$

$$m_2 \mathbf{v}^2_{2f} = m_1 \mathbf{v}_{2f} \left(\mathbf{v}_{1i} - \mathbf{v}_{1f} \right) \tag{10.8}$$

Eq: 10.6 may be written in the form

$$m_2 \mathbf{v}^2_{2f} = m_1 \mathbf{v}_{1i}{}^2 - m_1 \mathbf{v}^2_{1f}$$

$$= m_1 \left(\mathbf{v}^2_{2i} - \mathbf{v}^2_{1f} \right)$$

$$= m_1 \left(\mathbf{v}_{1i} + \mathbf{v}_{1f} \right) \left(\mathbf{v}_{1i} - \mathbf{v}_{1f} \right) \tag{10.9}$$

Equating the right side terms of (Eqs: 10.8 and 10.9)

$$m_1 \mathbf{v}_{2f} (\mathbf{v}_{1i} - \mathbf{v}_{1f}) = m_1 (\mathbf{v}_{1i} + \mathbf{v}_{1f}) (\mathbf{v}_{1i} - \mathbf{v}_{1f})$$

$$\mathbf{v}_{2f} = (\mathbf{v}_{1i} + \mathbf{v}_{1f}) \tag{10.10}$$

Substituting for $\mathbf{v}_{2f}$ in (Eq: 10.5)

$$m_1 \mathbf{v}_{1i} = m_1 \mathbf{v}_{1f} + m_2 (\mathbf{v}_{1i} + \mathbf{v}_{1f})$$

$$(m_1 + m_2) \mathbf{v}_{1f} = \mathbf{v}_{1i} (m_1 - m_2)$$

$$\mathbf{v}_{1f} = ((m_1 - m_2)/(m_1 + m_2)) \mathbf{v}_{1i} \tag{10.11}$$

Substituting the value of $\mathbf{v}_{1f}$ from (Eq: 10.11) in (Eq: 10.10)

$$\mathbf{v}_{2f} = \mathbf{v}_{1i} + ((m_1 - m_2)/(m_1 + m_2)) \mathbf{v}_{1i}$$

$$(m_1 + m_2) \mathbf{v}_{2f} = \mathbf{v}_{1i} (m_1 + m_2) + \mathbf{v}_{1i} (m_1 - m_2)$$

$$\mathbf{v}_{2f} = ((2m_1)/(m_1 + m_2)) \mathbf{v}_{1i} \tag{10.12}$$

(A) MASSIVE TARGET ($m_1 \ll m_2$)

(Eq: 10.11) reduces to

$$\mathbf{v}_{1f} = (-m_2)/(m_2)) \mathbf{v}_{1i} = \sim - \mathbf{v}_{1i} \tag{10.13}$$

(Eq: 10.12) reduces to

$$\mathbf{v}_{2f} = ((2m_1)/(m_2)) \mathbf{v}_{1i} \tag{10.14}$$

$$= \sim 0$$

The projectile bounces backward with approximately the same speed (Fig. 10.2). The velocity of the target is approximately zero. The massive target remains stationary. An example of this case is: if you throw a ping-pong ball at a wall or table head-on, it bounces backwards with approximately the same speed, whereas the wall or the table remains stationary.

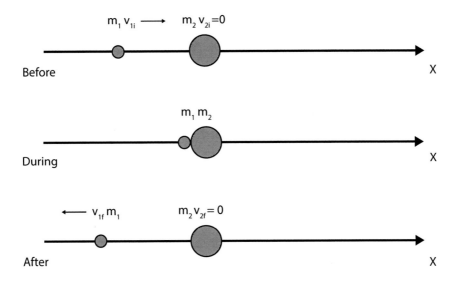

Figure 10.2: Elastic head-on collision of a light projectile and a heavy target at rest.

(B) EQUAL MASSES ($m_1 = m_2$)

(Eq: 10.11) reduce to

$$\mathbf{v}_{1f} = \sim 0 \tag{10.15}$$

(Eq: 10.12) reduces to

$$\mathbf{v}_{2f} = ((2m_1)/(2\ m_1))\ \mathbf{v}_{1i} \tag{10.16}$$

$$= \mathbf{v}_{1i}$$

After the collision, the projectile will be at rest and the target flies off with the velocity of the projectile. For a head-on collision of two billiard balls, one stationary and other moving, the stationary ball picks up the velocity whereas the projectile comes to a dead stop.

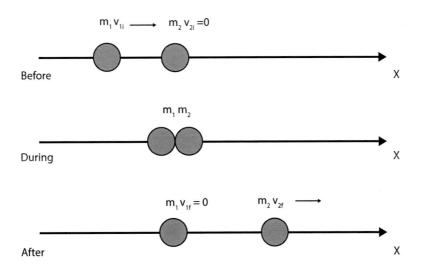

Figure 10.3: Elastic head-on collision between equal masses.
Projectile moving and the target at rest.

(C) MASSIVE PROJECTILE ($m_1 >> m_2$)

(Eq: 10.11) reduces to

$$\mathbf{v}_{1f} = \sim (m_1)/(m_1))\mathbf{v}_{1i} = \sim \mathbf{v}_{1i} \tag{10.17}$$

(Eq: 10.12) reduces to

$$\mathbf{v}_{2f} = ((2m_1)/(m_1)\mathbf{v}_{1i} \tag{10.18}$$

$$= \sim 2\,\mathbf{v}_{1i}$$

The massive projectile moves approximately with its initial velocity whereas the target moves with $\sim 2\,\mathbf{v}_{1i}$ and the direction will be same as $\mathbf{v}_{1i}$(Fig.10.4).

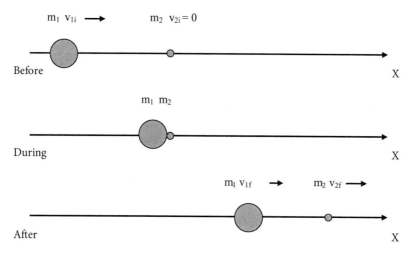

Figure 10.4: Elastic head-on collision between a massive projectile and a light target at rest.

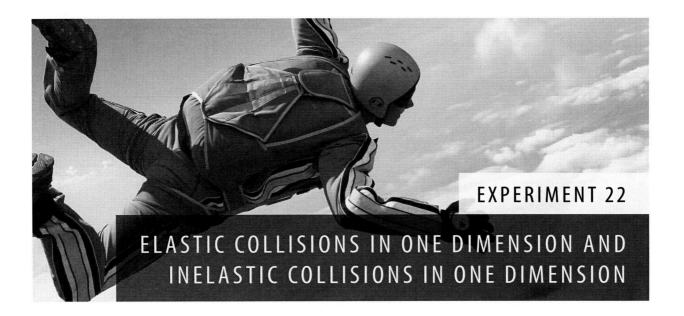

I.   Objective

To investigate the kinematics of elastic collisions in one dimension

II.   Equipment

Air track, gliders, photo-gates, and computer

III.   Experimental Details

You need a low friction arrangement to study the collisions. Therefore you will use an air track. Adjust the leveling screws of the air track to make it horizontal. Adjust the airflow rate such that the gliders can move friction free.

(a) Massive target ($m_1 << m_2$)

Use the gliders with elastic rubber bands, or fix good, elastic material to the gliders. Add an additional 2-kg on each side of the target glider. In order that the glider slides friction free, it is necessary that you put the weights on both sides of the glider. Remember that Eqs. (10.13) and (10.14) were obtained for the limiting case. For finite values of the masses, the final velocities may be slightly different from what had been obtained for the limiting cases. Measure the initial and final velocities of the projectile and the target before and after the collision. Collect and enter the data in *Table 10.1* for different values of $\mathbf{v}_{1i}$.

Using PASCO Capstone/Datastudio Software

SET-UP

Open *DataStudio*, click on *create experiment* option. Attach the photo-gate to the projectile launcher, then plug the photo-gate into digital channel 1. Next plug the receptor panel to channel 2. Click *setup* button on the top left corner. Click *choose interface* button. Select *Science Workshop* 500 interface. An image will now appear in the window. Select the left most yellow highlighted port (digital channel 1). Now select the "photo-gate" sensor option. Now select the digital channel 2 image and select the "photo-gate" sensor option. Now close the experiment setup window. When you are ready to start data collection hit the "start" button. When the two gliders collide you must stop the data collection and hit start again. This is to ensure that you have two separate velocity runs, before and after collision.

DATA ANALYSIS

In order to graph velocity you need to select the graph option under the displays menu of the bottom left hand corner. Select whichever run you want to measure under the velocity folder and hit ok. hit ok. You should see a point, which will represent the elapsed time.

Table 10.1: Elastic collisions in one dimension: (a) massive target ($m_1 << m_2$)

Note that v_{1i}, v_{2i}, v_{1f}, v_{2f} are vector quantities. Take them as positive if they are directed towards right (that is, in the positive x-direction) and negative if they are directed towards left (that is, in the negative direction).

Run #	m_1 (kg)	m_2 (kg)	V_{1i} (m/s)	V_{2i} (m/s)	V_{1f} (m/s)	V_{2f} (m/s)	Initial momentum p_i (kg. m/s)	Final momentum p_f (kg. m/s)	% change in momentum $\frac{(p_f - p_i)}{p_i}$ x100	Initial KE = ($\frac{1}{2}$) $m_1 v^2_{1i}$ (J)	Final KE= ($\frac{1}{2}$)$m_1 v^2_{1i}$ +($\frac{1}{2}$)$m_2 v^2_{2f}$ (J)	% change in KE $\frac{((KE_{final} - KE_{initial})}{KE_{initial})}$ x100

(b)   Equal masses ($m_1 = m_2$)

You will investigate the collision process when both the projectile and the target are of equal mass. Put equal weights on each of the glider. Put the weights on both sides of each glider; this will ensure that the gliders move smoothly. After adding weights to the glider, adjust the air flow if necessary to keep it moving with no friction. Keep the target glider stationary and give a gentle push to the projectile glider. You would notice that the projectile more or less comes to rest and the target glider flies off picking up the velocity of the projectile. Repeat the experiment with three equal weights added to each of the two gliders. Enter the data in *Table 10.2*.

Table 10.2: Elastic collisions in one dimension: (b) Equal masses ($m_1 = m_2$)

Note that $\mathbf{v}_{1i}$, $\mathbf{v}_{2i}$, $\mathbf{v}_{1f}$, $\mathbf{v}_{2f}$ are vector quantities. Take them as positive if they are directed towards right (that is, in the positive x-direction) and negative if they are directed towards left (that is, in the negative direction).

Run #	m_1 (kg)	m_2 (kg)	V_{1i} (m/s)	V_{2i} (m/s)	V_{1f} (m/s)	V_{2f} (m/s)	Initial momentum p_i (kg. m/s)	Final momentum p_f (kg. m/s)	% change in momentum $\frac{(p_f - p_i)}{p_i}$ x100	Initial KE = (½) $m_1v^2_{1i}$ (J)	Final KE= (½)$m1v^2_{1i}$ +(½)m_2 v^2_{2f} (J)	% change in KE $\frac{((KE_{final} - KE_{initial})}{KE_{initial}})$ x100
				0								
				0								
				0								
				0								

(c)   Massive Projectile ($m_1 \gg m_2$)

Note that (Eqs: 10.17 and 10.18) were obtained for the limiting values of $m_1 \gg m_2$. Put additional weights on the projectile and, by trial and error, keep the photo-gate at positions such that you can conveniently measure the initial velocity of m_1 and the final velocities of both the gliders m_1 and m_2 after the collision. Repeat the measurements for different values of $\mathbf{v}_{1i}$. Enter the data in *Table 10.3*.

Table 10.3: Elastic collisions in one dimension: (a) massive projectile ($m_1 \gg m_2$)

Note that $\mathbf{v}_{1i}$, $\mathbf{v}_{2i}$, $\mathbf{v}_{1f}$, $\mathbf{v}_{2f}$ are vector quantities. Take them as positive if they are directed towards right (that is, in the positive x-direction) and negative if they are directed towards left (that is, in the negative direction).

Run #	m_1 (kg)	m_2 (kg)	V_{1i} (m/s)	V_{2i} (m/s)	V_{1f} (m/s)	V_{2f} (m/s)	Initial momentum p_i (kg. m/s)	Final momentum p_f (kg. m/s)	% change in momentum $\frac{(p_f - p_i)}{p_i}$ x100	Initial KE = (½) $m_1v^2_{1i}$ (J)	Final KE= (½)$m1v^2_{1i}$ +(½)m_2 v^2_{2f} (J)	% change in KE $\frac{((KE_{final} - KE_{initial})}{KE_{initial}})$ x100
				0								
				0								
				0								
				0								

PART II.
INELASTIC COLLISIONS IN ONE DIMENSION

Kinetic energy is not conserved in inelastic collisions because part of the kinetic energy is converted to heat. However conservation of momentum is valid in both elastic and inelastic collisions. In inelastic collisions, the objects often stick together after the collision. A ballistic pendulum, where a bullet is fired into a suspended wooden block, is an example of an inelastic collision. Inelastic collisions are common in sub-atomic physics where part of the kinetic energy is used to excite the atoms/nuclei to higher energy states. As you would expect, inelastic collisions played an important role in the understanding of atomic/nuclear structure.

Put sticky clay "Velcro" to the ends of the gliders as shown. Push them from opposite sides in opposite directions such that they have approximately the same speed. Put the sticky clay such that the gliders stick together after the collision. If the gliders have approximately equal masses and equal speeds before the collision, you would find that they will come to rest after the collision. In this example, you could clearly see that the momentum is conserved but the kinetic energy is not conserved in the collision process. In this particular case, almost all the kinetic energy is converted into heat and the final kinetic energy is equal to zero. For different values of m_1 and m_2 and by gently pushing them in appropriate directions, you change their initial velocities. Notice that m_1 and m_2 stick together after the collision. Measure the initial velocities of m_1 and m_2 and the final velocity, v_f, of the combined mass, $m_1 + m_2$.

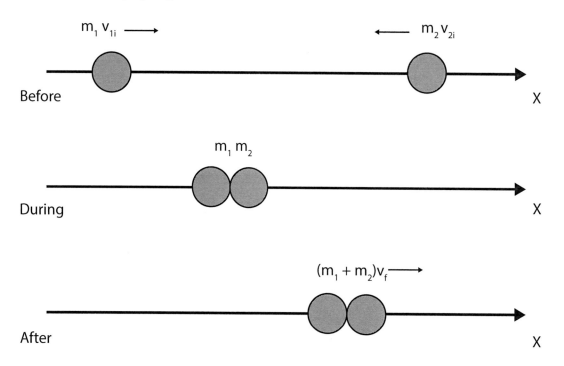

Figure 10.5: Inelastic collisions.

Table 10.4: Inelastic collisions in one dimension.
Momentum is conserved and the kinetic energy is not conserved

Note that $\mathbf{v}_{1i}$, $\mathbf{v}_{2i}$, $\mathbf{v}_f$ are vector quantities. Take them as positive if they are directed towards right (that is, in the positive x-direction) and negative if they are directed towards left (that is, in the negative direction).

Run #	m_1 (kg)	m_2 (kg)	V_{1i} (m/s)	V_{2i} (m/s)	V_f (m/s)	Initial momentum $(m_1v_{1i}+m_2v_{2i})$ p_i (kg. m/s)	Final momentum $(m_1+m_2)v_f$ P_f (kg. m/s)	% change in momentum $\dfrac{(p_f - p_i)}{p_i}$ x100	Initial KE $= (\frac{1}{2})$ $m_1v_{1i}^2 +$ $(\frac{1}{2})m_2v_{2i}^2$ (J)	Final KE= $(\frac{1}{2})(m_1+m_2)v_f^2$ (J)	% change in KE $\dfrac{((KE_{final} - KE_{initial})}{KE_{initial})}$ x100

Rotational Inertia

Experiments 23 & 24

Rotational Inertia

The kinematics of motion was described by a number of simple equations relating the displacement, velocity, acceleration and time. The dynamics of translational motion gave relationships between force, acceleration, and momentum. You performed several experiments covering translational motion. In the present chapter, you will study the kinematics and dynamics of rotational motion. For an object undergoing rotational motion about a fixed axis, one can readily identify the rotational analogues of the translational motion and write down the equations governing the kinematics and dynamics of rotational motion.

For translational motion, Newton's second law gives the relationship between the net force, **F**, and the induced translational acceleration, **a**.

$$\mathbf{F} = m\mathbf{a}$$

where m is the mass of the body, also called the body's inertial mass.

For rotational motion, the rotational analogue of mass is rotational inertia, also called moment of inertia. The moment of inertia of an object depends on the distribution of the mass of the object with respect to the axis of rotation. The rotational inertia

$$\Delta I = \Delta m\, r^2$$

where Δm is the mass located at a distance r from the axis of rotation. The rotational inertia is a linear function of the mass, Δm, and a quadratic function, r^2, of the radial distance, r, from the axis of rotation. One can calculate the rotational inertia of regular shaped objects by employing analytical integration methods. For irregular objects, one can employ numerical integration methods. The rotational analogues of the translational motion are given in *Table 11.1*.

Table 11.1: Rotaional analogues of the translational motion

Translational motion	Rotational motion
Inertial mass m	Rotational inertia I
Position vector **r**	Angular position θ
Force **F**	Torque τ
Linear velocity **v** (= d**r**/dt)	Angular velocity ω (= dθ/dt)
Linear acceleration **a** (= d**v**/dt)	Angular acceleration α (= dω/dt)
Linear momentum **p** (= m**v**)	Angular momentum **L** (= I ω)
The net force is equal to the rate of change of linear momentum $\mathbf{F}_{net} = d\mathbf{p}/dt$	The net torque is equal to the rate of change of angular momentum $\tau_{xt} = dL/dt$
If the net force is equal to zero, the rate of change of momentum dp/dt = 0, the linear momentum **p** is constant	If the net torque is equal to zero, the rate of change of angular momentum dL/dt = 0, the angular momentum **L** is constant
Work done W = **F** • **d**	Work done W = τ • θ
Power (constant force) P = **F** • **v**	Power (constant torque) P = τ • ω
The net force is equal to mass times the linear acceleration **F** = ma	The net torque is equal to the moment of inertia times the angular acceleration τ = I α
Kinetic energy for translational motion KE = (1/2) mv²	Kinetic energy for rotational motion KE = (1/2) I ω²

Rotational Inertia

The rotational inertia of a body depends on the distribution of its mass with respect to the axis of rotation. The moments of inertia of some regular geometric objects are given below. In each case, the mass of the object is m.

1. Moment of inertia of a point mass m at a distance r from the axis of rotation.

$$I_y = m r^2$$

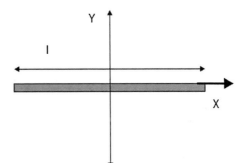

2. Moment of inertia of a small strip of mass m of length $d = R_2 - R_1$.

$$I_y = \frac{1}{2} m \left(R_1^2 + R_2^2 \right)$$

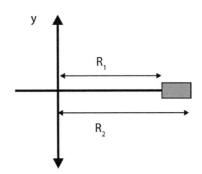

3. Moment of inertia of a thin rod of length l and mass m about an axis perpendicular to the rod (y-axis) and passing through its geometric center.

$$I_y = \frac{m l^2}{12}$$

4. Thin rectangular plate.

$$I_x = \frac{1}{12} m b^2$$

$$I_y = \frac{1}{12} m l^2$$

$$I_z = \frac{1}{12} (b^2 + l^2)$$

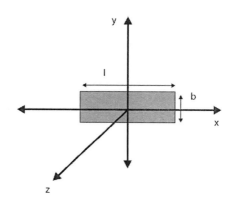

5. Moment of Inertia of a thin disk about an axis perpendicular to its geometric center of a thin disk of radius r and mass m.

$$I_x = \frac{1}{2} m r^2$$

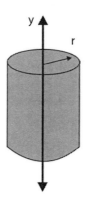

6. Moment of Inertia of a thin disk about an axis passing through its plane

$$I_y = \frac{1}{4} m r^2$$

7. Moment of inertia of a circular cylinder about its axis: r is the radius of the cylinder and m is its mass.

$$I_y = \frac{1}{2} m r^2$$

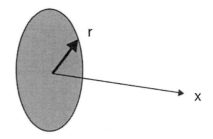

8. Moment of inertia of a regular sphere r is the radius of the sphere

$$I_x = I_y = \frac{2}{5}mr^2$$

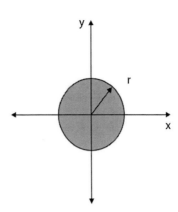

9. Moment of inertia of a ring/annular cylinder. About an axis passing through its center of mass and perpendicular to the plane of the ring. Let R_1 and R_2 respectively be the internal and external radii of the ring.

$$I_y = \frac{1}{2}m\left(R_1^2 + R_2^2\right)$$

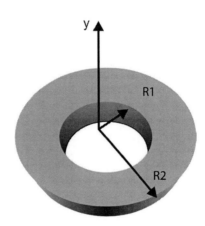

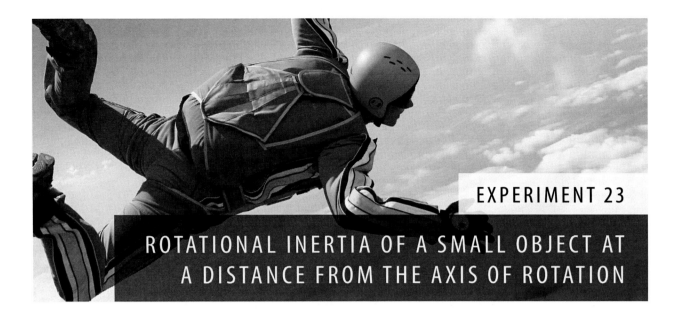

ROTATIONAL INERTIA OF A SMALL OBJECT AT A DISTANCE FROM THE AXIS OF ROTATION

I.   Objective

To measure the moment of inertia of a point mass located at a distance from the axis of rotation and compare it with the calculated value.

II.   Experimental

Using PASCO Capstone/Datastudio Software

SET-UP

Open *DataStudio*, click on *create experiment* option. Attach the photo-gate to the projectile launcher, then plug the photo-gate into digital channel 1. Next plug the receptor panel to channel 2. Click *setup* button on the top left corner. Click *choose interface* button. Select *Science Workshop* 500 interface. An image will now appear in the window. Select the left most yellow highlighted port (digital channel 1). Now select the "photo-gate" sensor option. Select the "constants" tab and put in the flag length. Now close the experiment setup window. Now on the top left hand corner under "data" you should have a "velocity" folder. When you are ready to start data collection hit the "start" button.

DATA ANALYSIS

In order to the velocity you need to select the graph option under the displays menu of the bottom left hand corner. Select whichever run you want to measure under velocity folder and hit ok. You should see a point, which will represent the velocity.

Measure the moment of inertia of a rotating platform and the moment of inertia of the platform plus the additional mass. Subtract the moment of inertia of the rotating platform from the moment of inertia of the platform plus mass to obtain the moment of inertia of the mass.

A. Moment of Inertia of the Rotating Platform

In the first part of the experiment, you measure the effective moment of inertia of the platform. The effective moment of inertia also includes the affects of the frictional forces on the rotational motion.

Apply a torque, τ, to the rotating platform by adding weights on the hanger

$$\tau = \mathbf{R} \times \mathbf{T} = R M (g - a) \tag{11.1}$$

where R is the radius of the pulley about which the thread is wound, M is the mass of the hanger and weights, and a is the linear acceleration of the weights (M). The torque induces an angular acceleration, α, on the platform such that

$$\tau = I_{platform} \alpha = I_{platform} \tag{11.2}$$

where, we have used the relationship between the linear acceleration, a, and the angular acceleration α
$$\mathbf{a} = R\alpha$$

From (Eqs: 11.1 and 11.2)

$$I_{platform} = \frac{R^2 M(g - a)}{a} \tag{11.3}$$

(Eq 11.3) gives the effective moment of inertia of the table. By measuring the angular acceleration for an applied torque, one can calculate the effective moment of inertia of the platform. The effective moment o f inertia includes t he effects of the frictional forces as well. Measure the radius of the pulley, R, using a Vernier caliper. The values of the linear acceleration, a, are obtained using a smart pulley arrangement or a motion detector setup. Enter data in *Table 11.2*.

Table 11.2: Moment of inertia of the platform about the axis of the platform

Run #	Mass M (kg)	Linear acceleration a (m/s^2)	Radius of the pulley R (m)	$I_{platform}$ $= R^2 M(g - a)/a$ (kg. m^2)

B. Moment of inertia of the platform plus a mass m kept at a distance r from the axis of rotation of the platform

The moment of inertia of mass m about its axis of rotation

$$I_m = m\, r^2 \tag{11.4}$$

If we apply a torque τ to the platform and the mass, it will induce an angular acceleration of the system such that

$$\tau = (I_{platform} + I_m) \tag{11.5}$$

Here, $I_{platform}$ is the effective moment of inertia of the platform and I_m is the moment of inertia of the mass, M, as used in Part A,

$$\tau = R_{pulley}\, T = R_{pulley}\, M\,(g - a') \tag{11.6}$$

Equating (Eqs: 11.5 and 11.6)

$$I_{platform} + I_{mass} = \frac{R^2 M(g-a')}{a'} \tag{11.7}$$

From (Eqs: 11.5 and 11.7)

$$I_m = \left(\frac{R_{pulley}^{\ 2}\, M\,(g-a')}{a'} - I_{platform}\right)$$

$$I_m = I_{platform+mass} - I_{platform} \tag{11.8}$$

$$h^I_{\ m} = I_{platform+mass} - I_{platform}$$

Here you will use the experimental value of Iplatform obtained from Part A given by (Eq: 11.3). You will calculate the values of Im from E q . (8) and compare them with the calculated values using (Eq: 11.4). Keep m at different positions from the axis of rotation and measure the rotational inertia of m for different values of the distance, r, from the axis of rotation

Enter the data in *Table 11.3* on the following page.

Table 11.3: Moment of inertia of the mass (m) about the axis of the platform

Run #	Mass M (kg)	Linear acceleration a´(m/s²)	mass added to platform (m) (kg)	Distance r (m)	$I_m = mr^2$ (kg-m²)	Radius of the pulley R_{pulley} (m)	$I_{platform}$ from Table 11.2 (kg-m²)	$I_{platform} + I_{mass}$ from Eq. 11.7 (kg-m²)	I_m from Eq. 8 (kg-m²)	% accuracy

$$\% \text{ Accuracy} = \frac{\text{Measured value (column 10)} - \text{Expected value (column 6)}}{\text{Expected value (column 6)}}$$

III. Questions

1. The mass provided has finite dimensions. Would the finite size of the mass affect your calculated value? How would you correct the calculated value for the finite size of the mass, *m*?

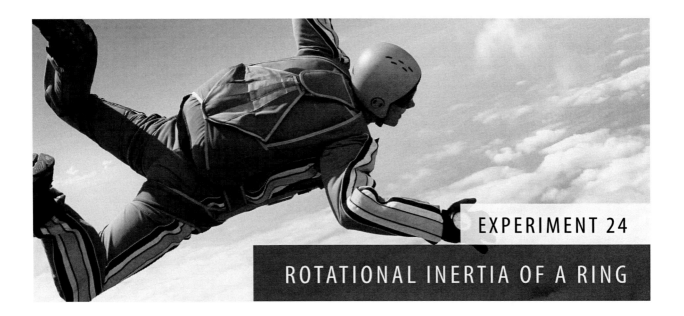

ROTATIONAL INERTIA OF A RING

I. Objective

To measure the moment of inertia of a ring about an axis passing through its geometric center and perpendicular to its plane and compare it with the calculated value.

II. Experimental

Measure the moment of inertia of a rotating platform and the moment of inertia of the platform plus the ring. Subtract the moment of inertia of the rotating platform from the moment of inertia of the platform plus ring to obtain the moment of inertia of the ring.

A. Moment of Inertia of the rotating platform

In the first part of the experiment, you measure the effective moment of inertia of the platform. The effective moment of inertia also includes the affects of the frictional forces.

Apply a torque, τ, to the rotating platform by adding weights on the hanger

$$\tau = R \, x \, T = R \, M \, (g - a) \tag{11.1}$$

Here, R is the radius of the pulley about which the thread is wound M is the mass of the hanger and weights, and a is the linear acceleration of the weight (M). The torque induces an angular acceleration on the platform such that

$$\tau = I_{platform} \, a = I_{platform} \left(\frac{a}{R} \right) \tag{11.2}$$

where, we have used the relationship between the linear acceleration, a, and the angular acceleration α
$$\mathbf{a} = R\alpha$$

From (Eqs: 11.1 and 11.2)

$$I_{platform} = \frac{R^2 M (g - a)}{a}$$

(11.3)

Measure the radius of the pulley, R, using a vernier caliper. The values of the linear acceleration, a, are obtained using a smart pulley arrangement or a motion detector setup. Enter data in *Table 11.4*.

Table 11.4: Moment of inertia of the platform

Run #	Weight M (kg)	Linear acceleration a (m/s²)	Radius of the pulley R (m)	$I_{platform}$ = $R^2 M(g - a)/a$

B. Moment of inertia of the platform plus the ring

The moment of the ring of mass m about its axis

$$I_r = \frac{1}{2} m (R_1^2 + R_2^2)$$

(11.4)

where m is the mass of the ring, R1 is the internal radius of the ring, and R2 is the external radius of the ring. If we apply a torque, τ, to the combined platform and the ring, it will induce an angular acceleration of the system such that

$$\tau = (I_{platform} + I_{ring}) \, \alpha'$$

$$\tau = (I_{platform} + I_{ring}) \left(\frac{\alpha}{R}\right)$$

(11.5)

Where α is the induced angular acceleration of the platform plus ring and a' is the linear acceleration of the weights. Here, Iplatform is the moment of inertia of the platform and Iring is the moment of inertia of the ring about the axis of rotation. The torque is applied by adding weights to the hanger. Let the mass of the weights and hanger be M. If a' is the linear acceleration of the weights, the tension in the string

$$T = M (g - a')$$

(11.6)

The torque acting on the platform

$$\tau = R \, x \, T$$

(11.7)

Substituting the for T from (Eq: 11.6) into (Eq: 11.7)

$$\tau = R_{pulley} \; x \; T = R_{pulley} \; M \; (g - a) \tag{11.8}$$

Equating the torques given by (Eq: 11.5) into (Eq: 11.8)

$$I_{platform} + I_{ring} = \frac{R^2 \; M \; (g - a')}{a'}$$

$$I_{ring} = \left(\frac{R^2_{pulley} \; M \; (g - a')}{a'} - I_{platform} \right) \tag{11.10}$$

$$I_{ring} = I_{platform + ring} - I_{platform}$$

Here, you will use the experimental value of the $I_{platform}$ obtained from Part A from *Table 11.4*, column 5. You will calculate the values of Iring from (Eq: 11.8) and compare them with the calculated values using (Eq: 11.5).

III.   Experimental

Keep the ring on the platform so that it rests in the groove. Let M be the mass of the weights plus hanger. The linear acceleration of the hanger is measured by a smart pulley arrangement or using a motion detector setup.

Collect data for different values of the torque by changing the weights, M.

Enter data in *Table 11.5*.

Using PASCO Capstone/Datastudio Software

SET-UP

Open *DataStudio*, click on *create experiment* option. Attach the photo-gate to the projectile launcher, then plug the photo-gate into digital channel 1. Next plug the receptor panel to channel 2. Click *setup* button on the top left corner. Click *choose interface* button. Select *Science Workshop* An image will now appear in the window. Select the left most yellow highlighted port (digital channel 1). Now select the "photo-gate" sensor option. Select the "constants" tab and put in the flag length. Now close the experiment setup window. Now on the top left hand corner under "data" you should have a "velocity" folder. When you are ready to start data collection hit the "start" button.

DATA ANALYSIS

In order to the velocity you need to select the graph option under the displays menu of the bottom left hand corner. Select whichever run you want to measure under velocity folder and hit ok. You should see a point, which will represent the velocity.

Table 11.5: Moment of inertia of the ring

Inner radius of the ring (R_1) = m

Outer radius of the ring (R_2) = m

Run #	Weight (kg)	Linear acceleration a´(m/s²)	Mass of the ring m (kg)	$I_m = (1/2)m$ $(R_1^2 + R_2^2)$	Radius of the pulley R_{pulley} (m)	$I_{platform}$ from Eq. 3	$I_{platform} + I_{ring}$ from Eq. 9	I_{ring} from Eq. 10	% accuracy

$$\% \text{ Accuracy} = \frac{\text{Measured value of } I_{in} \text{ (Table 2, column 9)} \quad - \quad \text{Calculated value of } I_{ring}}{\text{Calculated value of } I_{ring} \text{ (Table 2, column 5)}}$$

IV. Questions

1. Compare the moment of inertia of the platform ($I_{platform}$) with the expected value. If m is the mass of the platform, the moment of inertia of a thin disk about an axis passing through its geometric center and perpendicular to its plane is given by

   $I = (1/2)\, m\, R^2$

   Where, R is the radius of the disk.

2. Explain the possible reasons as to why the calculated value is different from the measured value. Identify possible systematic errors in your measurement.

Conservation of Angular Momentum

Experiments 25 & 26

CONSERVATION OF ANGULAR MOMENTUM BY REDISTRIBUTING MASS ON A ROTATING PLATFORM

I.   Introduction

Experiment 18 deals with the conservation of linear momentum. The rotational analog of linear momentum is angular momentum. Just as linear momentum, angular momentum is conserved in both elastic and inelastic collisions. Conservation of linear momentum and angular momentum are powerful laws of the physical world and are applicable from sub-atomic systems to planets and galaxies. These laws provided a wealth of information about the structure of atoms and atomic nuclei. In this experiment, you will investigate the conservation of angular momentum.

II.   Objective

Investigate the law of conservation of angular momentum by re-distributing a mass on a rotating platform.

III.   Theory

The rotational analog of Newton's second law states that the net torque acting on a body is equal to the time rate of change of the angular momentum.

$$\boldsymbol{\tau} = \frac{d\mathbf{L}}{dt}$$

If the net torque acting on the body is equal t o zero, then

$$\frac{d\mathbf{L}}{dt} = 0$$

or **L** is constant.

If the net torque acting on the body is equal to zero, the angular momentum of the system remains constant irrespective of the internal changes within the body. In this experiment, you will measure the initial angular momentum of a rotating platform and a mass and the final angular momentum of the platform with the mass redistributed and compare them.

Let,

$I_{platform}$ be the moment of inertia of the platform alone about an axis passing through its center of mass and perpendicular to the plane of the platform.

I_m be the moment of inertia of the mass alone about an axis passing through the center of mass of the platform and perpendicular to the plane of the platform

ω_i be the initial angular velocity of the platform and the mass

ω_f be the final angular velocity of the platform with the mass redistributed

L_i be the initial angular momentum of the platform + mass

L_f be the final angular momentum of the platform + mass (re-distributed)

The initial angular momentum of the disk and the mass

$$L_{initial} = (I_{platform} + mr_1^2)\, \omega_i \tag{12.1}$$

After you have moved the mass to a new position, let the final angular momentum of the combination be

$$L_{initial} = (I_{platform} + mr_1^2)\, \omega_f \tag{12.2}$$

When you have moved the mass, there will be no effect on the angular momentum of the system. You will compare the final angular momentum with the initial angular momentum of the system. If the angular momentum was conserved, it would agree within experimental errors. Compare the values given by (Eqs: 12.1 and 12.2).

To measure the moment of inertia, you will apply a known torque to the system and measure the angular speed induced.

IV.   Experimental Setup

Moment of Inertia of the Rotating Platform

In the first part of the experiment, you will measure the effective moment of inertia of the platform. The effective moment of inertia includes the effects of the frictional forces also.

Apply a torque, τ, to the rotating platform by keeping the weights on the hanger

$$\tau = R \: x \: T = R\,M\,(g - a) \tag{12.3}$$

Here, R is the radius of the pulley about which the thread is wound, M is the mass of the hanger and weights, and a is the linear acceleration of the weights (M). The torque induces an angular acceleration on the platform such that

$$\tau = I_{platform} \, \alpha = I_{platform} \left(\frac{a}{R}\right) \tag{12.4}$$

Here, we have used the relationship between the angular acceleration, α, and the linear acceleration, a,

$$a = R\,a$$

From (Eqs: 12.3 and 12.4)

$$I_{platform} = \frac{R^2\,M\,(g-a)}{a} \tag{12.5}$$

(Eq: 12.5) gives the moment of inertia of the platform where the frictional forces are also taken into account. Measure the radius of the pulley, R, using a Vernier caliper. The values of the linear acceleration, a, are obtained using the smart pulley arrangement. Enter data in *Table 12.1*.

Table 12.1: Moment of inertia of the platform about the axis of the platform.

Run #	Mass M (kg)	Linear acceleration a (m/s²)	Radius of the pulley R (m)	$I_{platform}$ = R²M(g – a)/a (kg-m²)

Part II. Conservation of Angular Momentum by Re-distributing Mass on a Rotating Platform

The moment of inertia of a point mass m about a vertical axis passing through the center of mass of the platform

$$I_m = m\,r_1^2 \tag{12.6}$$

If we apply a torque τ to the combined platform and the mass, by giving a spin with your hand, it will have an initial angular momentum L1 and let ω_1 be the initial angular speed. If you change the position of the mass by gradually pulling it in or by gradually releasing it to a new position, this would result in a change in the angular speed of the platform plus the mass.

The initial angular momentum is given by (Eq. 12.1) and the final angular momentum by (Eq. 12.2). We will calculate and compare the initial and final angular momenta as given by (Eqs. 12.1 and 12.2).

Level the apparatus and setup the photo-gate such that you can measure the time for one complete revolution. Spin the platform holding the rough surface at the bottom. As the platform attains a steady speed with no wobbling, measure the time for 2-3 oscillations and calculate the time period T1 for one oscillation. The angular velocity

$$\omega_i = 2\pi/T_1 \ (rad/s)$$

Pull the mass in or release it so that it is at a distance r2 from the axis of rotation. Measure the time period, T2, for an oscillation without disturbing the rotating platform. The final angular velocity

$$\omega_f = 2\pi/T_2 \ (rad/s)$$

Here, you will use the experimental value of the $I_{platform}$ obtained from Part A, *Table 12.1*, column 5. The value of I_m is obtained from (Eq: 12.4) to calculate the initial angular momentum of the platform and the mass. Keep *m* at a different position from the axis of rotation and obtain the new angular momentum. Measure the initial and final angular momenta for different initial rotational speeds. Different rotational speeds can be obtained by giving different spins to the platform using your hand

Enter data in *Table 12.2*. You will compare the value of *L* (column 5) with the value of the final angular Momentum, L_f (column 8).

Using Datastudio Software

SET-UP

Open *DataStudio*, click on *create experiment* option. Attach the photo-gate to the projectile launcher, then plug the photo-gate into digital channel 1. Next plug the receptor panel to channel 2. Click *setup* button on the top left corner. Click *choose interface* button. Select *Science Workshop* 500 interface. An image will now appear in the window. Select the left most yellow highlighted port (digital channel 1). Now select the "photo-gate" sensor option. Select the "constants" tab and put in the flag length. Now close the experiment setup window. Now on the top left hand corner under "data" you should have a "velocity" folder. When you are ready to start data collection hit the "start" button.

DATA ANALYSIS

In order to the velocity you need to select the graph option under the displays menu of the bottom left hand corner. Select whichever run you want to measure under velocity folder and hit ok. You should see a point, which will represent the velocity.

Table 12.2: Conservation of angular momentum.

The average value of the moment of inertia of the platform from Part I of the experiment (data from *Table 12.1*, column 5) =   .

Run #	Moment of inertia of the platform from Part I of the exp. (kg.m²)	Mass m (kg)	r_1 (m)	Initial angular velocity of the platform ω_i (rad/s)	L_i from (Eq: 12.1) (kg.m²/s)	r_2 (m)	Final angular velocity of the platform ω_f (rad/s)	L_f from (Eq: 12.2) (kg.m²/s)

V.   Questions

1. The ice skater sometimes gives herself a spin with stretched arms and then brings them closer to her body. What effect this maneuver would have on the rotational speed of her body?

2. A Merry-go-round has 12 persons symmetrically placed on the perimeter of a circular arc. When it is freely rotating about its axis, two persons occupying symmetric positions have suddenly jumped from the Merry-go-round. What effect would it have on the rotational speed of the Merry-go-round?

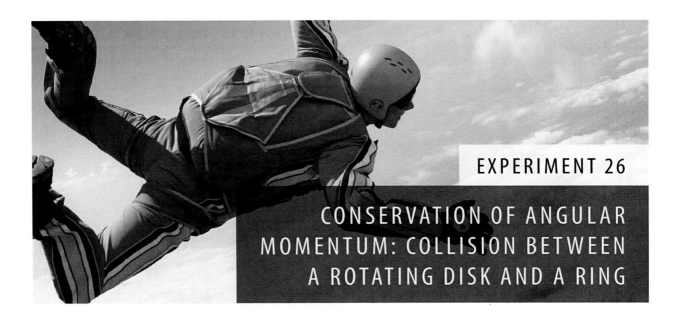

I.   Introduction

In experiment 18, you investigated the conservation of linear momentum. The rotational analog of linear momentum is the angular momentum. Just as linear momentum, angular momentum is conserved in both elastic and inelastic collisions. Conservation of linear momentum and angular momentum are powerful laws of the physical world that are applicable to sub-atomic systems and the motion of planets and galaxies as well. These laws provided a wealth of information about the structure of the atoms and the atomic nuclei. In this experiment, you will investigate the conservation of angular momentum.

Objective

Investigate the law of conservation of angular momentum by studying the collision between a rotating platform and a ring.

II.   Theory

The rotational analog of Newton's second law states that the net torque acting on a body is equal to the time rate of change of the angular momentum.

$$\tau = \frac{dL}{dt}$$

If the net torque acting on the body is equal t o zero, then

$$\frac{dL}{dt} = 0$$

or L is constant.

If the net torque acting on the body is equal to zero, the angular momentum of the body remains constant irrespective of the internal changes within the body. In this experiment, you will measure the initial angular momentum of a rotating disk and the final angular momentum of the disk plus a ring and compare them.

Let,

I_{disk} be the moment of inertia of the disk alone about an axis passing through its center of mass

and

perpendicular to the plane of the disk

I_{ring} be the moment of inertia of the ring alone about an axis passing through its center of mass

and perpendicular to the plane of the ring

ω_i be the initial angular velocity of the disk only

ω_f be the final angular velocity of the disk and the ring

L_i be the initial angular momentum of the disk

L_f be the final angular momentum of the disk plus ring

The initial angular momentum of the disk

$$L_i = I_{disk}\, \omega_i \tag{12.1}$$

After you dropped the ring on to the rotating disk, the final angular momentum of the combination

$$L_{final} = (I_{disk} + I_{ring})\, \omega_f \tag{12.2}$$

When you dropped the ring on to the disk, the torque acting on the disk and the ring forms an equal and opposite pair and cancel each other. This will have no effect on the angular momentum of the system. Since the ring itself is not rotating initially, the initial angular momentum of the system is equal to the angular momentum of the disk. You will compare the final angular momentum of the disk plus ring system with the initial angular momentum of the disk. If the angular momentum were conserved, they would agree within the experimental errors. You compare the values given by Eqs. (1) and (2).

The moment of inertia of the disk about an axis passing through its center of mass and perpendicular to the plane of the disk.

$$I_{disk} = \frac{1}{2} M R^2 \tag{12.3}$$

Here, M is the mass of the disk and R is its radius.

The moment of inertia of the ring of mass m about an axis passing through its center of mass and perpendicular to the plane of the ring is

$$I_{ring} = \frac{1}{2} m\, (R_1^2 + R_2^2) \tag{12.4}$$

Here R_1 and R_2 are the internal and external radii and m is the mass of the ring.

III. Experimental Setup

Using PASCO Capstone/Datastudio Software

SET-UP

Open *DataStudio*, click on *create experiment* option. Attach the photo-gate to the projectile launcher, then plug the photo-gate into digital channel 1. Next plug the receptor panel to channel 2. Click *setup* button on the top left corner. Click *choose interface* button. Select *Science Workshop* 500 interface. An image will now appear in the window. Select the left most yellow highlighted port (digital channel 1). Now select the "photo-gate" sensor option. Select the "constants" tab and put in the flag length. Now close the experiment setup window. Now on the top left hand corner under "data" you should have a "velocity" folder. When you are ready to start data collection hit the "start" button.

DATA ANALYSIS

In order to the velocity you need to select the graph option under the displays menu of the bottom left hand corner. Select whichever run you want to measure under velocity folder and hit ok. You should see a point, which will represent the velocity.

Level the apparatus and setup the photo-gate head as shown in Fig. (1). Give the disk a spin using your hand. Measure the initial angular velocity, ωi, using the photo-gate assembly. Hold the ring just above the disk, drop the ring into the grove on the disk and measure the final angular velocity, ωf. Repeat the experiment for different values of the initial angular velocity. Enter data in Table 1.

Setup the photo-gate such that you can measure the time for a certain number of revolutions. Spin the platform holding the rough surface at the bottom. As the platform attains a steady speed with no wobbling, measure the time for 2-3 oscillations and calculate the time period, T1, for one oscillation. The angular velocity

$$\omega_i = 2\pi/T_1 \text{ (rad/s)}$$

Measure the time for 2-3 oscillations without disturbing the rotating platform. Calculate the time period T2. The final angular velocity

$$\omega_f = 2\pi/T_2 \text{ (rad/s)}$$

Table 12.3: Conservation of angular momentum

Run #	Mass of the disk M (kg)	Radius of the disk R (m)	I_{disk} Eq.(3) (kg.m²)	ω_i (rad/s)	L_i from Eq.(1) (kg. m²/s)	Mass of the ring m (kg)	R_1 (m)	R_2 (m)	I_{ring} Eq. (4) (kg.m²)	ω_f (rad/s)	L_f Eq. (2) (kg. m²/s)

IV. Questions

1. Compare the initial rotational kinetic energy of the disk with the final rotational kinetic energy of the disk plus ring. Is the rotational mechanical energy of the system conserved in this experiment? If it is not conserved , explain why?

2. The ice skater sometimes gives herself a spin with stretched arms and then brings them closer to her body. What effect this maneuver would have on the rotational speed of her body?

3. A Merry-go-round has 12 persons symmetrically placed on the perimeter of a circular arc. When it is freely rotating about its axis, two persons occupying symmetric positions have suddenly jumped from the Merry-go-round. What effect would it have on the rotational speed of the Merry-go-round?

4. You have calculated the moment of inertia of the disk using (Eq: 12.3), which is actually valid for a solid disk. The disk provided to you has a groove. Calculate the moment of inertia of the disk provided to you wherein you will take account of the groove in the disk as well.

Equilibrium of a Body

Experiments 27 & 28

EQUILIBRIUM OF A RIGID BODY

I. Introduction

We often talk about the mechanical equilibrium of bridges, buildings, trucks etc. In this experiment, you will investigate the equilibrium of objects in general.

Force is responsible for the translational acceleration of a body and if the body is to be in translational equilibrium, the net force acting on the body must be equal to zero.

$$\Sigma \mathbf{F} = 0$$

Force is a vector quantity and may be resolved into components along the x, y and z-axes. For the body to be in translational equilibrium, the net force along each of the x, y and z-axes should be separately equal to zero.

$$\Sigma F_x = 0, \qquad\qquad \Sigma F_y = 0, \qquad\qquad \text{and } \Sigma F_z = 0$$

Torque is responsible for the angular acceleration and if the body is to be in rotational equilibrium, the net torque, $\boldsymbol{\tau}$, acting on the body must be equal to zero.

$$\Sigma \tau = 0$$

The torque, τ, being a vector quantity may also be resolved into its components along the x, y and z-axes. For the body to be in rotational equilibrium, the net torque along each of the x, y, and z-axes must be separately equal to zero.

$$\Sigma \tau_x = 0, \qquad\qquad \Sigma \tau_y = 0, \qquad\qquad \text{and } \Sigma \tau_z = 0$$

For a body to be in equilibrium, in general both the conditions for translational and rotational equilibria have to be satisfied.

$\Sigma F = 0$, $\Sigma F_x = 0$, $\Sigma F_y = 0$,   and $\Sigma F_z = 0$,

$\Sigma \tau = 0$ $\Sigma \tau_x = 0$, $\Sigma \tau_y = 0$,   and $\Sigma \tau_z = 0$

II. Torque

Torque is a vector quantity and is defined with respect to the axis of rotation. Consider a mass, m, represented by a vector, **r**, from the origin of a Cartesian Co-ordinate system. If a force, **F**, is acting on the mass, m, the torque about the origin

$\tau = \mathbf{r} \times \mathbf{F}$

If θ is the angle **F** makes with **r**, the magnitude of the torque about the origin is

$|\tau| = |\mathbf{r}||\mathbf{F}| \sin \theta$

The direction of the torque is given by the right hand thumb rule or right hand screw rule. For the directions of **r** and **F** shown in Fig. 13.1, the direction of the torque will be out of the page along the positive z-axis.

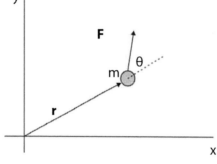

Figure 13.1

Example

Let us consider a light and rigid beam of negligible mass supported by a sharp edge with masses suspended from the beam as shown. What is the condition that the beam will be in equilibrium?

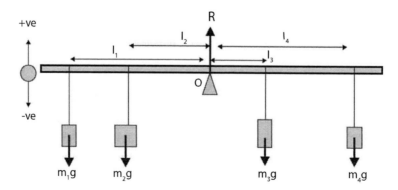

Figure 13.2

For translational equilibrium, the net force acting on the beam should be equal to zero.

$$\Sigma F_y = 0$$

Taking the forces directed upwards as positive and the forces directed downwards as negative, we get

$$- m_1 g - m_2 g - m_3 g - m_4 g + R = 0 \tag{13.1}$$

$$R = +m_1 g + m_2 g + m_3 g + m_4 g \tag{13.2}$$

There will be a normal reaction force R acting on the sharp edge directed upwards as shown.

The torque due to the force $m_1 g$ about O is in the anti-clock wise direction and we take it as positive. This torque will be directed out of the page towards you. The torque due to the force $m_3 g$ about O is in the clockwise direction and we take it as negative. This torque is directed into the page.

For rotational equilibrium, the net torque about any point on the beam or outside the beam must be equal to zero. One can calculate the torques from any axis of rotation though we often choose a convenient axis. Let us calculate the torques about O. Note that the beam and the forces are perpendicular to each other. Taking the torques (moment of the forces) about an axis passing through O and perpendicular to the page

$$\Sigma \tau_o = 0$$

$$l_1 m_1 g + l_2 m_2 g - l_3 m_3 g - l_4 m_4 g = 0 \tag{13.3}$$

The normal reaction force, R, is passing through O and therefore it will have no torque about O. (Eqs: 13.1 and 13.3) can be solved for any two unknown quantities. You may choose any convenient axis of rotation instead of O to obtain the condition for rotational equilibrium.

If you also wish to take into account the mass of the beam, we can easily modify the above equation. Let m be the mass per unit length of the beam. We will assume that the beam is made up of the same material and is of uniform cross section. In this case, the mass per unit length of the beam is constant over its entire length. If l is the length of the beam left of O to the left end, then the length of the beam right of O will be (100 -l) if we use a meter stick for the beam. (Eq: 13.1) will be modified as

$$-m_1 g - m_2 g - m_3 g - m_4 g - mg + R = 0 \tag{13.4}$$

(Eq: 13.3) will be modified as

$$l_1 m_1 g + l_2 m_2 g + \frac{l}{2} l \mu g - l_3 m_3 g - l_4 m_4 g - \frac{(100 - l)}{2} (100 - l) \mu g = 0 \tag{13.5}$$

III. Experimental

PART I
Equilibrium of a meter-stick with two known applied forces

In this experiment, first you will find the center of gravity (CG) of a meter stick and support the meter stick at the CG using a knife-edge. You will suspend two known masses on either side of the point of the knife-edge. By adjusting the positions of the masses, obtain the equilibrium condition (the meter scale is horizontal and stable). You will apply the conditions for translational and rotational equilibrium.

1. Make sure that the knife-edge clamp is removed from the meter-stick and determine the mass of the meter stick using a weighing scale.

2. Determination of the center of gravity of the meter stick: Fix the knife-edge clamp on the meter stick and place the assembly with the knife-edge on the support. By adjusting the clamp, balance the meter stick on the support. The position of the knife-edge gives the location of the center of gravity (CG) of the meter stick.

3. Keeping the meter stick supported at its CG, suspend a mass, m_1, of 0.100 kg at 0.4 m on one arm of the meter stick. Slide a mass, m_2, of 0.200 kg on the other arm of the meter stick such that the meter stick with the weights is balanced. Note the position of the 0.200-kg mass on the meter stick.

Repeat the experiment for different values of m_1 and m_2. Keep m_1 at some fixed position on one arm of the meter stick and slide m_2 on the other arm until the condition for balance is achieved. Enter data in *Table 13.1*. The torques may be calculated about any suitable axis. Here, the torques are calculated about an axis perpendicular to the page and passing through the CG of the meter stick. Since the knife-edge supports the meter stick at its center of gravity (C. G.) , if we take moments about the knife-edge, the moments of the weight of the meter stick and the normal reaction at the knife-edge will be zero because both of them pass through the point about which the moments are taken. For this experimental arrangement, m_2 and m_4 are zero in (Eqs: 13.1 and 13.3).

Table 13.1: Rotational equilibrium of a meter stick with two known forces applied. The distance from the knife-edge to the mass m_1 is l_1 and the distance from the knife-edge to mass m_3 is l_3.

Run #	Position of CG l (m)	m_1 (kg)	l_1 (m)	m_3 (kg)	l_3	Torque anticlockwise (+ve) $m_1 g l_1$ (N.m)	Torque clockwise (- ve) $m_3 g l_3$ (N.m)

The condition for translational equilibrium, (Eq: 13.4) reduces to

$$-m_1 g - m_3 g - mg + R = 0 \tag{13.6}$$

Where R is the normal reaction at the knife-edge, which coincides with the CG of the meter stick and m its mass.

Part II
Equilibrium of a meter stick with three known forces applied

Support the meter-stick at its C.G. Choose any masses m_1, m_2, and m_3. Keep m_1 and m_2 in one arm, say left of C.G of the meter stick at some positions of your choice. Adjust the position of m_3 and its magnitude if necessary on the other arm such that the meter stick with weights is balanced about its point of support at its C.G. Repeat the experiment for three sets of m_1, m_2, and m_3. Enter data in *Table 13.2.*

Table 13.2: Rotational equilibrium of a meter stick with three known forces applied.
l_1, l_2, and l_3 are measured from the knife-edge.

Run #	Position of C.G (m)	m_1 (kg)	l_1 (m)	m_2 (kg)	l_2 (m)	m_3 (kg)	l_3 (m)	Torque anticlockwise $(m_1 g l_1 + m_2 g l_2)$ (+ve) $m_2 g l_2$ (N.m)	Torque clockwise (- ve) $m_3 g l_3$ (N.m)

The condition for translational equilibrium, (Eq: 13.4) reduces to

$$-m_1 g - m_2 g - m_3 g - mg + R = 0 \tag{13.7}$$

The condition for rotational equilibrium, Eq. (3) reduces to

$$l_1 m_1 g + l_2 m_2 g - l_3 m_3 g = 0$$

PART III
Determination of the mass of the meter-stick

Support the meter stick at some suitable position other than its center of gravity. Take two unequal masses, say 0.2 kg and 0.3 kg. Suspend one of the masses from one arm of the meter stick and slide the second mass on the other arm of the meter stick until the equilibrium condition is achieved. By intuition or by trial and error, you should be able to guess which of the weights should be on which arm. Let μ be the mass per unit length of the meter stick. Enter data in *Table 13.3*. Repeat the experiment with two sets of values of m_1 and m_2. Let l be the length of the meter stick to the left of the knife edge, then $(100 - l)$ will be the length of the meter stick to the right of the knife-edge.

Table 13.3: Determination of the mass of the meter stick

Run #	m_1(kg)	l_1(m)	m_3(kg)	l_3(m)	Position of knife edge l (m)

(Eq: 13.5) reduces to

$$l_1 m_1 g - l_3 m_3 g + \frac{l}{2}l\mu g - \frac{100-l}{2}(100-l)\mu g = 0$$

Knowing l_1, m_1, l_3, m_3, l, the mass per unit length, μ, of the meter stick can be calculated. The mass of the meter stick $m = \mu \times$ length of the meter-stick (=1 m)

Measure the mass of the meter stick using a weighing scale. This will be your true value. Compare the true value with the measured value.

$$\%Accuracy \quad = \quad \frac{\text{Measured value - True value (from weighing scale)}}{\text{True value (from weighing scale)}} \quad x\ 100$$

Home Assignment:

1. In part I, calculate the torques about an axis other than the CG and check whether the rotational equilibrium condition is satisfied. (Note: The moment of the reaction force, R, about an axis other than the CG will not be zero.)

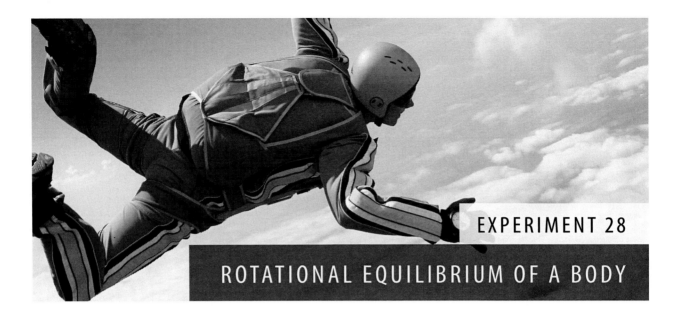

ROTATIONAL EQUILIBRIUM OF A BODY

I.   Introduction and Objective

In this experiment, you will investigate the rotational equilibrium of a body about an axis. We will use a PASCO model ME-8949 equal arm balance. We will apply torques on the arm and show that for rotational equilibrium, the net torque acting on the body is equal to zero.

Torque is responsible for the angular acceleration about an axis and if the body is to be in rotational equilibrium, the net torque, τ , acting on the body about the axis must be equal to zero.

II.   Theory

Torque is responsible for the angular acceleration about an axis and if the body is to be in rotational equilibrium, the net torque, $\boldsymbol{\tau}$, acting on the body about the axis must be equal to zero.

$\Sigma\boldsymbol{\tau} = 0$

The torque, $\boldsymbol{\tau}$, being a vector quantity may be resolved into its components along the x, y and z-axes. For the body to be in rotational equilibrium, the net torque along each of the x, y, and z-axes must be separately equal to zero.

$\Sigma\boldsymbol{\tau}_x = 0$ $\Sigma\boldsymbol{\tau}_y = 0$ and $\Sigma\boldsymbol{\tau}_z = 0$

Therefore, for a body to be in rotational equilibrium, the conditions to be satisfied are:

$\Sigma\boldsymbol{\tau} = 0$ $\Sigma\boldsymbol{\tau}_x = 0,$ $\Sigma\boldsymbol{\tau}_y = 0,$ and $\Sigma\boldsymbol{\tau}_z = 0$

III. Torque

Torque is a vector quantity and is defined with respect to the axis of rotation. Consider a mass, m, represented by a vector **r** , from the origin of a Cartesian Coordinate system. If a force, F, is acting on the mass, *m*, the torque about the origin

$$\tau = \mathbf{r} \times \mathbf{F}$$

If θ is teh ange F makes with r, the magnitude of the torque about the origin is

$$|\tau| = |r||F|\sin\theta$$

The direction of the torque is given by the right hand thumb rule or right hand screw rule. For the directions of r and F shown in *Fig 13.1*, the direction of the torque will be out of the page along the positive z-axis.

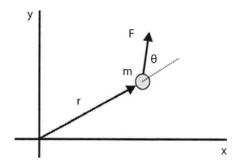

Figure 13.1 Torque acting on a body of mass m.

IV. Equipment

The PASCO Model 8949 Equal Arm Balance, weight hangers, weights, a long thread with strands, a stand to hold the balance.

V. Experimental

Clamp the brass support rod to a rigid clamp and a stand. Make sure that the beam rotates about the axis freely with no friction. When the beam is in equilibrium and horizontal, keep a thread with two strands at the lower part of the beam. You will use the thread as a reference to note whether the beam is horizontal or not. If you have access, you can use a low power (1/2 mW) Helium-Neon laser beam as a horizontal level indicator. If you employ a laser, make sure you will never look directly into the laser beam. Apply about 100 grams of weight to one of the loops on the right on the bottom of the arm. Apply weights on the left side of the arm to one of the bottom loops and adjust the weights by trial, and error until the arm is horizontal. Repeat the measurements for different weights and different loops, each time obtaining the equilibrium condition. Enter the data in *Table 13.4*.

Part 1: For a body to be in rotational equilibrium, the net torque actin on the body is equal to zero. Put known load say on the left arm on one of the holes and balance the beam by putting loads on the right 3 holes one at a time. Measure the perpendicular distance from the axis of rotation to the point of application of the force (*Fig 13.2*). Calculate the torques in the anticlockwise direction as positive and the clockwise direction as negative and find the net torque on the body. Enter data in *Table 13.4*.

Table 13.4 Rotational Equilibrium of a body

S #	Weights on the right to the axis of rotation					Weights on the left to the axis of rotation				
	Weight mg	Loop #	Position vector r	$r_\perp$	$\tau = -r_\perp F$	Weight mg	Loop #	Position vector r	$r_\perp$	$\tau = +r_\perp F$

Note that **r** is the position vector from the axis of rotation to the point where **F** is applied. θ is the smaller angle the force makes with respect to the direction of the position vector. The direction of the torque is obtained from the right hand rule. The torque in the clockwise direction = $-rF \sin \theta$ which is equal to $-r_\perp \times F$. Similarly the torque in the clockwise direction is equal to $+r_\perp \times F$. Therefore, to compare the torques you don't have to measure the angle θ and it is adequate if you measure $r_\perp$.

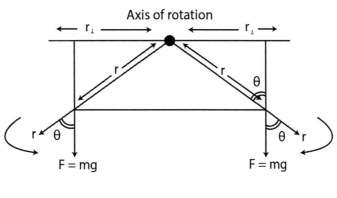

Anticlockwise direction
Torque is taken as positive
$\tau = +r F \sin\theta$

Clockwise direction
Torque is taken as negative
$\tau = -r F \sin\theta$

Figure 13.2: The net torque acting on the beam.

Part 2: Calculate the mass of the unknown object by applying the condition that for a body to be in equilibrium, the net torque acting on the body is equal to zero. Put the unknown load on the left arm and balance the beam by adding weights on the right arm by trial and error at one of the holes on the right arm at a time. Each time calculate the unknown load (mg) and mass by applying the condition, the net torque acting on the body is equal to zero.

Simple Harmonic Motion

Experiment 29

I.   Introduction and Objectives

We notice in our everyday lives that a number of objects oscillate about their equilibrium positions. A swing goes back and forth, a chandelier oscillates about a mean position, a weed swings back and forth, a plucked string oscillates about its equilibrium position, and so on. The atoms and molecules in solids vibrate about their mean positions as well. Oscillating electric and magnetic fields result in electromagnetic radiation.

II.   Theory

Let us define a few terms related to oscillatory motion. Let us consider an object such as a mass attached to a spring or the bob of a simple pendulum oscillating in one plane. The distance, $x(t)$, of the object from its equilibrium position is the displacement. The maximum displacement is called the amplitude. One oscillation corresponds to a complete to-and-fro motion of the object from some initial position of the object to when it returns to the same position moving in the same direction. The time it takes to complete one oscillation is called the time period, T. The number of oscillations in a unit time (1-second) is known as the frequency, f. The frequency is measured in oscillations per second, or simply Hertz (Hz). If the object (or the field) is oscillating at regular intervals of time then it is called periodic motion, which is also known as harmonic motion. If the periodic motion is sinusoidal, it is called simple harmonic motion (SHM). In the following, we present details of the simple harmonic motion. Even though the displacement, velocity and acceleration are vector quantities, we will treat them as scalar quantities since we are considering one dimensional motion only.

The time period

$$T = \frac{1}{f} \qquad (14.1)$$

where f is the frequency.

The displacement of a particle, $x(t)$ (x as a function of time t), executing simple harmonic motion in one dimension may be expressed as a sine or a cosine function of time, t,

$$x(t) = A \sin (\omega t + \varphi) \qquad (14.2)$$

where $x(t)$ is the displacement, which is a function of time, A is the amplitude, ω is the angular frequency, t is the time, and Φ is the phase constant. The angular frequency

$$\omega = 2\pi f \qquad (14.3)$$

has the units of rad/s. It turns out that most of the natural systems execute harmonic motion when they are perturbed from their equilibrium position.

The velocity

$$v(t) = dx/dt = A\omega \cos (\omega t + \varphi) \qquad (14.4)$$

and the acceleration

$$a(t) = -A\omega^2 \sin (\omega t + \varphi) \qquad (14.5)$$

$$= - \omega^2 x(t) \qquad (14.6)$$

This is a basic equation characteristic of simple harmonic motion. The instantaneous acceleration, $a(t)$, is equal to the instantaneous displacement, x(t), times the square of the angular frequency, ω, and is oppositely directed. In the following, you will investigate the simple harmonic motion of (1) a mass attached to a spring and (2) a simple pendulum.

An example of simple harmonic motion is given by the projection of a uniform circular motion on a diameter of its circle. This also gives us a simple non-calculus based derivation for the acceleration, a, of a particle undergoing simple harmonic motion. Let us consider the uniform circular motion of a particle moving in a circle of radius A with an angular velocity

$$\omega = (\Delta\theta / \Delta t)$$

At time t, the angular position of the particle is $(\omega t + \varphi)$ where φ is the phase angle at $t = 0$. As the particle executes uniform circular motion, the projections of the position vector, P, on the x and y-axes (or simply the x and y-components of the position vector) executes simple harmonic motion. The x-component of the position vector as a function of time t may be written as

$$x(t) = A \cos(\omega t)$$

where we have assumed $\varphi = 0$ at t = 0.

The centripetal acceleration of the particle directed towards the center of the circle

$$a = (v^2/A) = A \omega^2 .$$

The instantaneous x-component of the acceleration

$$a(t) = -A\omega^2 \cos(\omega t + \varphi) \tag{14.5}$$

$$= -\omega^2 x(t) \tag{14.6}$$

Oscillations of A Mass Attached To A Spring Horizontally

Consider a mass m on a frictionless horizontal surface connected to a spring. If we stretch the spring a small distance, x, from its un-stretched position and release, it will execute oscillatory motion. If we further assume that the spring is massless and ideal (internal frictional forces of the spring are negligible), the spring exerts a force on the mass

$$F(x) = -kx \quad \text{(Hooke's Law)} \tag{14.7}$$

where x is the displacement of the mass from its equilibrium position, and k is the force constant of the spring. The value of k depends on the stiffness of the spring. The negative sign indicates that the force exerted by the spring is opposite in direction to the displacement of the mass. For example, if the displacement x is positive (to the right) the force exerted by the spring will be in the $-x$ direction (to the left) and vice versa.

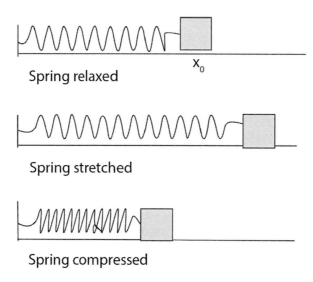

Spring relaxed

x_0

Spring stretched

Spring compressed

Figure 14.1: Oscillations of a mass attached horizontally to a spring.

When you pull the mass, the work done in stretching the spring is stored as potential energy of the spring. As the mass is released, the spring force pulls the mass towards the un-stretched position. When the mass reaches the un-stretched position, all the potential energy of the spring is converted into the kinetic energy of the mass. The kinetic energy of the mass is converted into the potential energy of the spring as the spring is compressed again.

The spring force gives rise to the acceleration of the mass

$$a(t) = \frac{F(t)}{m} = \frac{-kx(t)}{m} \tag{14.8}$$

Note that $a(t)$ means the acceleration, a, is a function of time. Similarly $F(t)$ indicates the force as a function of time t.

Assuming that the oscillations of the spring-mass system are simple harmonic, we equate the acceleration given by (Eqs: 14.6 and 14.8)

$$-\frac{-kx(t)}{m} = -\omega^2\, x(t)$$

$$\omega = 2\pi f = \sqrt{k/m} \tag{14.9}$$

the frequency

$$f = \frac{1}{2\pi}\sqrt{k/m} \tag{14.10}$$

(Eq: 14.10) gives a relationship between the spring constant k, the mass m and the frequency of the simple harmonic motion. The time period

$$T = 2\pi\,\sqrt{m/k} \tag{14.11}$$

SIMPLE HARMONIC MOTION OF A MASS SUSPENDED VERTICALLY AND A MASS ATTACHED HORIZONTALLY TO A SPRING ON AN AIR TRACK

I.   Introduction

In Part I of this experiment, you will attach weights to a vertically suspended spring and measure the elongation of the spring as a function of the force applied. From these data, you will be calculating the force constant of the spring.

In Part II, you will allow a mass attached to the spring to oscillate vertically and measure the displacement as a function of time for 10-20 oscillations using a motion detector. You will investigate whether the motion is simple harmonic or not, and you will measure the frequency of the oscillating mass.

OBJECTIVES

1.   Measure the force constant of a spring.

2.   Investigate the nature of the oscillations of a mass attached to a spring suspended vertically and measure the frequency of the oscillations of the spring and mass system.

II.   Equipment

Springs, weights, motion detector, computer

Using PASCO Capstone/Datastudio Software

SET-UP

Open *DataStudio*, click on *create experiment* option. Attach the photo-gate to the projectile launcher, then plug the photo-gate into digital channel 1. Next plug the receptor panel to channel 2. Click *setup* button on the top left corner. Click *choose interface* button. Select *Science Workshop* 500 interface. interface. An image will now appear in the window. Select the left most yellow highlighted port (digital channel 1). Now select the "motion sensor" sensor option. Now close the experiment setup window. Now on the top left hand corner under "data" you should have position, velocity, and acceleration folders. When you are ready to start data collection hit the "start" button. For part III select the setup button and replace the motion sensor with the photo-gate in digital channel 1.

DATA ANALYSIS

In order to graph position you need to select the graph option under the displays menu of the bottom left hand corner. Select the run you want to graph under the parameter heading you want and hit ok. Then fit the graph with an appropriate curve. For parts II and III you need to graph position, velocity, and acceleration vs. time.

PART I
Force constant of a spring

The Force Constant of a Spring

Suspend a spring vertically and attach a mass, m, at its end. Hold the mass by hand and release it gradually at its equilibrium position. Let the elongation of the spring from its mean position be x.

Since the mass, m, is in equilibrium, the net force acting on the mass is equal to zero. The gravitational force acting on the mass ($= mg$) is equal in magnitude and opposite to the restoring force, F, of the spring.

If the applied force is within the elastic limit of the spring, the restoring force of the spring, F, is proportional to the elongation, x, of the spring and is oppositely directed with respect to x. This is known as Hooke's law.

$$F(x) = -kx \quad \text{(Hooke's Law)} \tag{14.7}$$

where F is the restoring force of the spring and x is the displacement of the spring from its equilibrium (un-stretched) position. The proportionality constant k is called the spring constant. If F is in Newtons and x in meters, the spring constant, k. will be in Newtons per meter (N/m).

The equilibrium condition may be written as

$$+ F_{spring} - mg = 0$$

If we increase the external force to, say, $2mg$, the elongation of the spring increases by a factor of 2 and so does the restoring spring force.

MOTION DETECTOR

The motion detector works as an automatic ranger. It measures the instantaneous distance from the detector to an object that reflects the ultrasonic waves. Ultrasonic waves are sound waves at high frequencies and are not audible to the human ear. The motion detector emits ultrasonic waves in the form of pulses with a cone angle of approximately 30°. The ultrasonic wave pulses are reflected from the surface of an object and are detected by the detector. The time difference from the emission of the pulse to the detection of the reflected pulse is measured. Knowing that the speed of sound in air at room temperature (20° C) is 343.9 m/s or 1238 km/h, one can calculate the distance from the motion detector to the object. A built-in software calculates the distance and tabulates the data. Since the time can be measured to a high precision (> 1μs), the distance, in turn, can be monitored quite precisely. By sending successive ultrasonic pulses, one can determine the distance as a function of time.

Open the motion detector software. For this part of the experiment, you will <u>not</u> set the mass oscillating and you will instead be measuring the elongation of the spring as a function of the applied force, F. If the mass of the hanger plus the weights is m (kg), the force will be mg (N). First you will put some weights, say, m_0 (hanger + say 0.020 kg) so that the spring will be straight and without kinks. Measure the position, x_0, of the weight using the motion detector. Since the mass is stationary, you would expect to get an approximately horizontal line on the displacement versus time plot. Add weights in increments of, say, 20 gm and for each additional weight, measure the new position, x_n, of the weights using the motion detector. Since, you are measuring the distance from the motion detector, (x_0-x_n) will give the elongation of the spring corresponding to the weights added. Subtract x_n from x_0 to obtain the elongation of the spring. Repeat this procedure until you collect 5-6 readings. Collect data for three different springs of different spring constants. Enter the data in Tables 14.1-3. You are advised to enter the data directly in the Excel worksheet and complete the data analysis and the plots.

Table 14.1: Force constant of spring #1.
Mass of the hanger and the weights added to keep the spring without kinks = ………kg and the corresponding reading of the motion detector = ………(x_0).

Run #	Additional weights m (kg)	Force due to additional weights $F = mg$ (N)	Initial position of the mass x_0 (m)	Final position of the mass x_n (m)	Elongation = Initial reading– Final reading $x = (x_0 - x_n)$ (m)	Force Constant $k = F/x$ (N/m)

Table 14.2: Force constant of spring #2.
Mass of the hanger and the weights added to keep the spring without kinks = ...kg and the corresponding reading of the motion detector = ...(x_0).

Run #	Additional weights m (kg)	Force due to additional weights $F = mg$ (N)	Initial position of the mass x_0 (m)	Final position of the mass x_n (m)	Elongation = Initial reading– Final reading $x = (x_0 - x_n)$ (m)	Force Constant $k = F/x$ (N/m)

Table 14.3: Force constant of spring #3.

Run #	Additional weights m (kg)	Force due to additional weights $F = mg$ (N)	Initial position of the mass x_0 (m)	Final position of the mass x_n (m)	Elongation = Initial reading– Final reading $x = (x_0 - x_n)$ (m)	Force Constant $k = F/x$ (N/m)

Plot a curve between applied force, F, along the y-axis and elongation along the x-axis for the spring #1 and fit the data to a linear equation. The slope of the curve gives the force constant, k, for spring #1. Plot similar curves for spring #2 and 3 and obtain the corresponding spring constants for them.

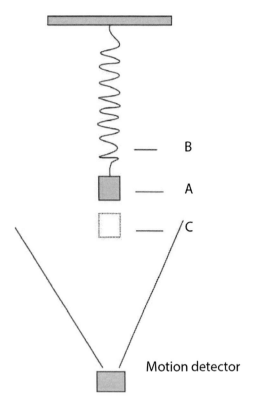

Figure 14.2 Experimental arrangement for measuring the spring constant using a motion detector.

PART II
Oscillations of a mass suspended vertically by means of a spring

I.   Introduction and Objective

The oscillations of a mass attached to a vertically suspended spring are an example of simple harmonic motion. Employing such a setup, you will measure and study a number of physical parameters related to simple harmonic motion.

OBJECTIVE

To investigate the nature of the oscillations of a mass attached to the end of a spring suspended vertically.

II.   Theory

Consider a mass, m, attached to a spring suspended vertically. If the weight of the mass is within the elastic limit of the spring, the spring will be stretched and the mass will reach an equilibrium condition. The forces acting on the mass are the gravitational force acting vertically downwards and the restoring force due to the spring acting in the opposite direction. Let the equilibrium position be A (Fig. 14.2). If you lift the mass to the position B by your hand and gently release it, the mass will undergo oscillations. At B, the kinetic energy of the mass is zero, and both the potential energy of the spring and the gravitational potential energy of the mass are at a maximum. At A, the kinetic energy of the mass is at a maximum, whereas the potential energy of the spring is equal to zero. At C, the kinetic energy of the mass is zero, the potential energy of the spring is at a maximum, and the gravitational potential energy is negative with respect to the mean position. At intermediate positions, part of the energy is in the form of kinetic energy, and part of the energy is in the form of the potential energy of the spring and the gravitational potential energy of the mass.

The mass, m, is acted on by two forces: (i) the force due to gravity (= mg) and the restoring force due to the spring. In this experiment, you will lift the mass vertically by a couple of cm and release it so that it executes oscillatory motion. As the mass oscillates, the gravitational potential energy of the mass as well as the potential energy of the spring change as a function of time. However, it can be shown that if you measure the displacement from the equilibrium position of the mass after it was suspended from the spring, the motion is still SHM.

If F is the net force acting on the mass, the acceleration experienced by the mass is due to the net force F acting on it. If we replace the spring force by the net force, one can use the expressions already derived for the acceleration (Eq: 14.8), frequency (Eq: 14.10) and the time period (Eq: 14.11).

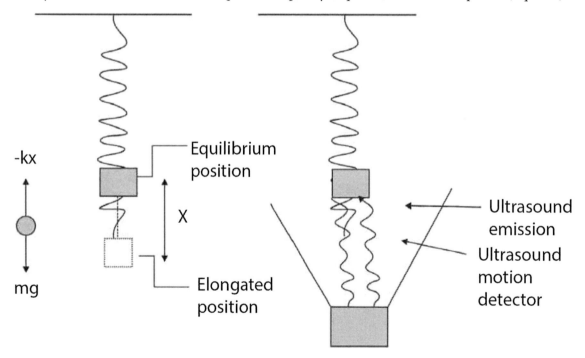

Figure 14.3: Spring constant of a spring.   **Figure 14.4:** Oscillations of a spring.

Suspend a mass, m_0, to the spring such that there are no kinks in the spring. Hold the mass, m_0, raise it upward vertically by a couple of cm, and release it. It will have oscillatory motion. By keeping the motion detector as shown, collect data for a certain duration of time (10 – 15 s). Adjust the sampling rate to 10-20 samples per second. If the sampling rate is too high, you are likely to get spikes in your data. If the sampling rate is too low, the plots may not be smooth. Choose an appropriate sampling rate. Plot the curves showing the functional relationships

a. distance vs. time

b. velocity vs. time

c. acceleration vs. time

What can you conclude from the plots?

The motion is said to be simple harmonic if the displacement, $x(t)$, is a sinusoidal function of time with a single frequency. Answer the following questions:

1. Are the displacement, velocity and acceleration of the spring executing vertical oscillations sinusoidal functions?

2. Do they have a single frequency? If they have multiple frequencies, how do these curves look?

3. What is the time period? You can obtain the time period by measuring the time between two crests or troughs of the wave, or measure the time for, say, five oscillations and calculate the time period (for one oscillation).

4. What is the frequency of the oscillator?

5. One oscillation corresponds to 2π radians. You notice that the displacement, velocity and acceleration curves begin at different parts of the wave at the time $t = 0$. They are said to differ in phase. Estimate the phase constants of the displacement, velocity and acceleration plots in radians. Estimate the phase difference of the velocity and acceleration plots with respect to the displacement curve.

The amplitude of a wave is defined as the maximum displacement from its mean position. You can calculate the value by measuring the peak to peak distance and dividing by two. Measure the amplitudes of the displacement, velocity and acceleration plots. Enter the data in *Table 14.4*.

6. Using the measured values of the amplitude and frequency from the displacement vs. time graph, calculate the corresponding amplitudes of the velocity and the acceleration from Eq. 14.4 using Eqs. 14.4 and 14.5 as detailed below

$$v_{max} = A\omega \qquad (14.12)$$

where A is the amplitude and ω is the angular frequency.

From (Eq: 14.5), the maximum value of the acceleration

$$a_{max} = - A\,\omega^2 \qquad (14.13)$$

Compare these calculated values of v_{max}, and a_{max} with the corresponding directly measured values. The measured values can be obtained by measuring directly v_{max} and a_{max} from the plots or from the computer fits.

Table 14.4: Values of amplitude, frequency and phase read directly from the plots.

Details of the plots	amplitude	frequency	phase
$x(t)$			
$v(t)$			
$a(t)$			

Computer Fits to the data

1. Fit the displacement versus time data to a sine function of the type Y= A*sin(B*x+C)+D and obtain the best fitted values of the amplitude (A), angular frequency (B), the phase (C) and the constant D.

   You will compare the constants in the fitted equation Y= A*sin(B*x+C)+D with Eq. (2) obtained for the displacement of a simple harmonic oscillator, $x(t) = A \sin(\omega t + \varphi)$.

   Using the best fitted values of A, B, C, and D, obtain the values of the (a) amplitude (b) the frequency and (c) the phase of the simple harmonic motion of the spring mass system and enter the data in *Table 14.5*.

2. Fit the velocity versus time data to a sine function of the type Y= A*sin(B*x+C)+D and obtain the best fitted values of the constants A; B, C, and D. Compare the fitted equation Y= A*sin(B*x+C)+D with (Eq: 14.4) obtained for the velocity as a function of time obtained for a simple harmonic oscillator, $x(t) = A\omega \cos(\omega t + \varphi')$. It does not matter whether you fit the data to a sine or cosine function since they differ by only a phase factor $\pi/2$ which can be taken into account by the new phase term (φ'). From the fitted data obtain the best-fitted values of the amplitude (A), angular frequency (B), the phase (C) and the constant D and enter the values in *Table 14.5*.

3. Fit the acceleration versus time data to a sine function of the type Y= A*sin(B*x+C)+D and obtain the best fitted values of the constants A, B, C, and D. Compare the fitted equation Y= A*sin(B*x+C)+D with Eq. (5) obtained for the acceleration as a function of time obtained for a simple harmonic oscillator, $v(t) = -A\omega^2 \sin(\omega t + \varphi)$. From the fitted data obtain the best-fitted values of the amplitude (A), angular frequency (B), the phase (C) and the constant D and enter the values in *Table 14.5*.

From each of the print out of the displacement vs. time, velocity vs. time and acceleration vs. time plot calculate the angular frequency, amplitude of the wave, and the phase constant and enter the data in *Table 14.5*. Compare the calculated values with the computer fitted values.

Table 14.5: Comparison of the best computer fitted values with the manually calculated values

	Displacement vs. time data		Velocity vs. time data		Acceleration vs. time data	
	Computer fitted values	Measured from the plots	Computer fitted values	Measured from the plots	Computer fitted values	Measured from the plots
Angular frequency (ω)						
Amplitude						
Phase C						
Constant D						

1. Notice from (Eq: 14.11) that the time period is independent of the amplitude of the oscillations. Verify this by measuring the time period for different amplitudes keeping m and k constant. Enter the data in a Table. Do you expect the time period T to be independent of large oscillations? Comment.

2. Notice from (Eq: 14.10) that the frequency f is inversely proportional to $\sqrt{m}$. You can measure the frequency as a function of mass and using the relation (Eq: 14.10) and the plot, you can obtain a more precise value for the spring constant.

    Squaring both sides of (Eq: 14.10) one gets

$$f^2 = \frac{k}{4\pi^2 \, m}$$

For different values of m, measure the corresponding values of the frequency. You get the values of the angular frequency ω directly from the computer fits. Calculate the frequency $f = \omega / 2 \times \pi$. Plot a curve between f^2 vs. $1/4\pi^2 m$. You will find it convenient to use the Excel software for the calculations and the plot. Enter the data f^2 and m in two separate columns. Obtain an x-y scatter plot of f^2 vs. $1/4\pi^2 m$. Fit the data to a linear function and obtain the slope. The slope of the straight line gives the value of the spring constant. Compare this value with the value obtained for the same spring in Part 1 as well as the mean of the values obtained from the fifth column of *Table 14.6*.

Table 14.6: Spring constant using the relationship between frequency and mass

S. No.	m (kg)	frequency f (Hz)	f^2 (1/s^2)	$k = 4\pi^2 \, mf^2$ (kg/s^2)

III. Calculations

CONSERVATION OF THE TOTAL MECHANICAL ENERGY

a. Transfer the data to an Excel Spreadsheet and calculate the potential energy of the spring as a function of time, t.

    $U(t) = (1/2) \, k \, [x(t)]^2$
    where k is the spring constant. Please note x(t) signifies that x is a function of time and not x multiplied by t.

b. Calculate the kinetic energy of the mass as a function of time, t

    $KE(t) = (1/2) \, m [v(t)]^2$

c. Calculate the gravitational potential energy as a function of time E(t)

$$PE(t) = mgx(t)$$

where x is taken positive upwards and negative downwards with respect to the mean position of the spring.

d. Calculate the total mechanical energy of the system

$$ME(t) = UE(t) + KE(t) + PE(t)$$

Plot $UE(t)$ vs.t , KE (t) vs. t, PE(t) vs. t , and ME (t) vs. t on the same graph.

Comment on the possible phase shifts between $UE(t)$, $KE(t)$ and $PE(t)$. Is the total mechanical energy, $ME(t)$, of the system conserved? Give your comments.

SIMPLE HARMONIC MOTION OF A MASS ATTACHED HORIZONTALLY TO A SPRING ON AN AIR TRACK

I.   Introduction and Objectives

The oscillations of a mass attached to a spring horizontally is an example of simple harmonic motion. Employing such a setup, you will measure and study a number of physical parameters related to simple harmonic motion.

II.   Materials

Air track, glider, weights, motion detector, flag attachment to the glider

III.   Experimental

Using a level indicator, adjust the air track so that it is horizontal. The schematic of the experimental arrangement is shown in Fig. 14.1. Attach the spring to one of the fixed arms of the air track and the glider to the other end of the spring. Add additional weights evenly on both sides of the glider. Connect a flag to the glider so that a motion detector may be used to measure the displacement vs. time data. Make sure that the central axis of the spring and the glider are in the same horizontal plane. Attach the flag on the glider. Compress the spring by about 1 cm and then release it. You will notice that the glider has oscillatory motion about its mean position. Collect the data for about 20 oscillations. Follow the analysis given in Part II of this experiment. In this case, verification of the conservation of mechanical energy is much simpler because the glider is moving horizontally and the change in the gravitational potential energy is zero. {Plot the displacement vs. time, velocity vs. time and the acceleration vs. time plots. Enter the data in Tables 14.3, 14.4, and 14.5 as detailed in the text in Part II of this experiment.}

CONSERVATION OF THE TOTAL MECHANICAL ENERGY

In this case, the gravitational potential energy remains constant because the oscillating mass (the glider) is at the same gravitational potential during its oscillations.

a. Transfer the data to an Excel Spreadsheet and calculate the potential energy of the spring as a function of time, t.

UE(t) = (1/2) k [x(t)]^2 where k is the spring constant .

b. Calculate the kinetic energy of the mass as a function of time, t

KE(t) = (1/2) m [v(t)]^2

c. Calculate the total mechanical energy of the system

ME(t) = UE(t) + KE(t).

Plot UE(t) vs. t, KE(t) vs. t, and ME(t) vs. t on the same graph. Comment on the possible phase shifts between UE(t), and KE(t). Is the total mechanical energy, ME(t), of the system conserved? Give your comments.

IV. Questions

1. In Fig. 14.2, A is the equilibrium position of the mass and B and C are the extreme positions. Identify at what positions of the oscillating mass (A, B, or C), displacement, velocity and acceleration will be (a) maximum and (b) minimum.

2. Notice that the displacement, velocity and acceleration curves are out of phase with each other. Do you expect them to have different phases? Explain the physical significance of the observed phase shifts.

3. From your data, investigate the dependence of the frequency, f, of the spring mass system with the mass, m. Equation (14.10) shows that $f = (1/2\pi)\sqrt{(k/m)}$. Plot f vs. $1/\sqrt{m}$ and investigate their functional relationship.

4. We have neglected the mass of the spring. However, if the mass of the spring is not negligible, how would your results be affected?

5. We assumed that the spring is ideal. In reality, as you stretch and compress the spring, frictional forces of the spring come into play. Explain how the frictional forces of the spring would or could affect your measurements.

Simple Pendulum

Experiments 30 & 31

I.   Introduction and Objectives

A bob of mass m suspended by means of a light inextensible string is commonly known as a simple pendulum. The pendulum is made to oscillate back and forth by displacing the bob by a small angle θ from its equilibrium position and releasing it.

II.   Theory

Let m be the mass of the bob and L the length of the simple pendulum. The time it takes to complete one oscillation is the time period, T. Let us consider the forces acting on the mass, m, when it is at the position B.

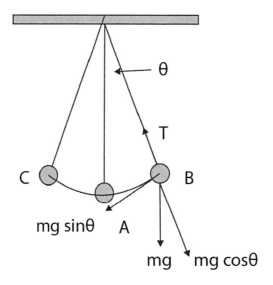

Figure 15.1 Simple Pendulum

The gravitational force, mg, acts vertically downwards and the tension, T, acts along the string in the direction shown (Fig. 15.1). We resolve the gravitational force into its components one along the tangent to the path and another along the radial direction as shown in Fig. 15.1. The tangential component ($= mg \sin \theta$) is directed towards the equilibrium position and is the restoring force. This is an equilibrium position and the bob is instantaneously at rest. The torque acting on the bob

$$\tau = - Lmg \sin \theta = I\alpha \tag{15.1}$$

where I is the moment of inertia of the bob about the axis of rotation O and α is the angular acceleration.

$$I = mL^2 \tag{15.2}$$

and $\alpha = d^2\theta/dt^2$

Substituting $\sin \theta \approx \theta$ and the values of I and α in (Eq. 15.1)

$$\frac{d^2\theta}{dt^2} = -\frac{g}{L}\theta \tag{15.3}$$

The solution of this differential equation may be written in the form

$$\theta(t) = \theta_0 \sin(\omega t + \phi) \tag{15.4}$$

where $\theta(t)$ is the angular displacement, θ_0, is the angular amplitude, ω, is the angular frequency, φ is the phase constant

$$d\theta/dt = \theta_0 \omega \cos(\omega t + \phi)$$

$$d^2\theta/dt^2 = \theta_0 \omega^2 \sin(\omega t + \phi) = -\omega^2\theta \tag{15.5}$$

Equating the right hand sides of (Eqs: 15.3 and 15.5)

$$-\omega^2\theta = -(g/L)\theta$$

$$\omega^2 = (g/L) \tag{15.6}$$

$$\omega = 2\pi f = \sqrt{(g/L)}$$

$$f = \frac{1}{2\pi}\sqrt{\frac{g}{L}} \tag{15.7}$$

$$T = 2\pi\sqrt{\frac{L}{g}} \tag{15.8}$$

$$T^2 = 4\pi^2 L/g \tag{15.9}$$

$$\omega = \sqrt{\frac{g}{L}} \qquad f = \frac{1}{2\pi}\sqrt{\frac{g}{L}} \qquad T = 2\pi\sqrt{\frac{L}{g}}$$

In the following two experiments, you will measure the time period (T) of a simple harmonic oscillator and experimentally investigate some of the functional relationships derived above.

I. Objectives

Part I

Investigate the dependence of the time period of a simple pendulum (T) on (a) the angular displacement, (b) the mass of the bob, and (c) the length

Part II

Investigate the conservation of mechanical energy using simple pendulum

II. Equipment

Simple pendulum, photo-gates, and computer

III. Experimental Details

Arrange the photo-gate at the equilibrium position of the bob of the simple pendulum as shown in Fig. 15.5. Give a small amplitude displacement to the bob and make sure that the bob does not hit the photo-gate as it oscillates about the mean position. After a couple of attempts, you should be able to get the condition that the simple pendulum more or less oscillates in a plane. However if you find it difficult or time consuming to attain this condition, take two strings and tie them as shown in the Fig. 15.5. This arrangement should enable you to keep the oscillations of the simple pendulum in a plane more easily.

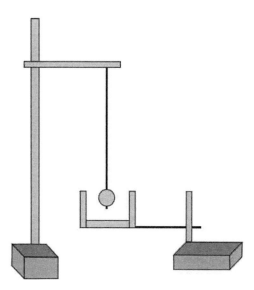

Figure 15.2: Experimental arrangement of a simple pendulum with a photo-gate arrangement.

Use the Pendulum Timing Software. The timing will begin when the photo-gate is first interrupted. The timing will continue until the photo gate is interrupted twice more. This will directly give you the time period for one oscillation of the simple pendulum.

Using PASCO Capstone/Datastudio Software

SET-UP

Open *DataStudio*, click on *create experiment* option. Attach the photo-gate to the projectile launcher, then plug the photo-gate into digital channel 1. Next plug the receptor panel to channel 2. Click *setup* button on the top left corner. Click *choose interface* button. Select *Science Workshop* 500 interface. An image will now appear in the window. Select the left most yellow highlighted port (digital channel 1). Now select the "photo-gate and pendulum" sensor option. Now close the experiment setup window. Now on the top left hand corner under "data" you should have a folder for "period" and one for "velocity". When you are ready to start data collection hit the "start" button.

DATA ANALYSIS

In order to graph the period and velocity you need to select the graph option under the displays menu of the bottom left hand corner. Select whichever run you want to measure under the specific folder and hit ok.

Part I
Dependence of the time period of
a simple pendulum (T) on

a. **the angular displacement**
b. **the mass of the bob and**
c. **the length**

(a) Time period (T) is independent of the angular amplitude (for small angular displacements)

The time period T is defined as the time an oscillator takes to complete one oscillation. In Fig. 15.1, if the bob is moving right, beginning at A, to B, crossing A in the opposite direction to C and then to A moving to the right is one oscillation. Measure the time period of the simple pendulum for different angular amplitudes. Adjust the length of the simple pendulum to about 1-m and measure the time period T for different small amplitudes, say 3, 5, 8, and 10 cm. For each value of the amplitude, collect data for about 30 oscillations and calculate the time period (T), the time taken for one oscillation. Enter data in *Table 15.1.*

Table 15.1: Time period versus angular amplitude.

Run #	Amplitude (m)	Time for 30 oscillations(s)	Time period T(s)
1	0. 02		
2	0. 04		
3	0. 06		
4	0. 08		
5	0. 10		

(b) The time period (T) is independent of the mass/material of the bob

Using bobs of different masses, measure the corresponding time period (T). You may choose bobs of wood, cork, iron, copper, steel, aluminum or whatever is available in the laboratory. For all the measurements keep the angular displacement small (~5°). Enter the data in *Table 15.2*. You may perform this part of the experiment using a simple pendulum of any convenient length about 60-100 cm.

Table 15.2: Time period and its dependence on the mass/material of the bob.

Run #	Material of the bob	Mass of the bob (kg)	Time for 30 oscillations(s)	Time period T(s)
1				
2				
3				
4				
5				

(c) Time period (T) dependence on the length of the simple pendulum

At a given place, since the acceleration due to gravity is constant, the time period (T) is directly proportional to $\sqrt{L}$ where L is the length of the simple pendulum (Eq: 15.7). For different values of L measure the corresponding values of T and enter the data in **Table 15.3**. Compare the values of T^2/L with the values of the last column, which is a constant that is equal to $4\pi^2/g$. Plot the data T^2 on the y-axis and L on the x-axis. Fit the data to a linear equation $y = Ax + B$. A good fit to a linear equation shows that T^2 is proportional to the length of the simple pendulum L and the slope of the straight line is a constant equal to $4\pi^2/g$.

Table 15.3: Time period versus length of the simple pendulum using a photo-gate.

Run #	Length of the pendulum L (m)	Time for 30 oscillations (s)	Time period T(s)	T^2 (s^2)	T^2/L (s^2/m)	$4\pi^2/g$
1						
2						
3						
4						
5						
6						

Part II
Conservation of Mechanical Energy Using Simple Pendulum

Simple pendulum is a good example for the investigation of the conservation of mechanical energy. As the simple pendulum oscillates, when the bob is at the position B (Fig. (3)), the bob has a potential energy ($= mgh$) and the kinetic energy is zero. You can measure the potential energy with respect to any reference point. We choose the equilibrium position of the simple pendulum as the reference point. As the bob swings back and forth, the potential energy at B is converted to kinetic energy at the position A, which in turn is converted back to the potential energy at the position C. The simple pendulum has maximum potential energy and no kinetic energy at the positions B and C whereas it has maximum kinetic energy and no potential energy at the position A. This process keeps on repeating until the simple pendulum loses its energy due to the frictional and resistive forces. At intermediate positions between A and B, the simple pendulum has intermediate values of both kinetic and potential energies. The mechanical energy of the system, that is, the sum of the potential and the kinetic energies, remains constant over its entire path if we neglect the losses due to frictional and resistive forces.

For the calculation of the potential energy, take the equilibrium position of the bob as the reference point. Using the photo-gate software, measure the velocity of the bob as it passes through its equilibrium position. You will measure the time taken by the bob to cross the LED beam of the photo-gate. Knowing the diameter of the bob, one can calculate the velocity of the bob as it crosses the photo-gate. Using a protractor, measure the angle θ and release the bob for values of θ = 5°, 10°, 15°, and 20°. For each angle, as the bob passes through the photo-gate, measure the corresponding velocity. Enter data in *Table 15.4*.

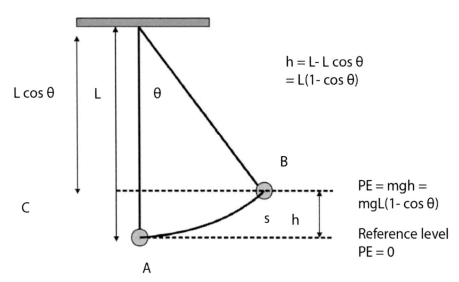

Figure 15.3: Conservation of mechanical energy using a simple pendulum.

If θ is the angular displacement (Fig. 15.3), the potential energy at the position B is = *mgh* = *mgL* (1 - cos θ). Enter the data on an Excel spreadsheet and complete the calculations.

Table 15.4: Conservation of mechanical energy using simple pendulum.

Run #	Mass of the bob m (kg)	θ (degrees)	L (m)	Potential energy at $B = mgL$ $(1 - \cos \theta)$ (J)	Velocity at A v_{max} (m/s)	Kinetic energy at $A = (\frac{1}{2}) mv^2_{max}$ (J)	% Deviation= $\dfrac{KE\text{-}PE}{PE}$ x 100
		5°	1 m				
		10°	1 m				
		15°	1 m				
		20°	1 m				

IV. Questions

From the plot T^2 versus length (L) (Part Ic), fit the data to a linear equation $y = mx + c$ and obtain the fitted value of the slope of the straight line. The slope of the curve is expected to be $= 4\pi^2/g$. Calculate the acceleration due to gravity g from the slope of the curve and compare it with the expected value. What is the percent accuracy of the measurement?

1. In Part (b) of the experiment, you investigated the time period versus angular displacement. Did you observe any systematic correlation between the time period (T) and the angular displacement? Why small angular amplitudes are important for the measurement of the time period of a simple pendulum?

2. For small amplitudes, it was stated that the time period is independent of the angular amplitudes. One student remarked that if the displacement is large, the bob travels longer distance and therefore the time period should increase with the increase in the amplitude. Give your answer or comments on her question.

SIMPLE HARMONIC MOTION OF A SIMPLE PENDULUM USING A MOTION DETECTOR

I.   Introduction and Objectives

A bob of mass m suspended by means of a light inextensible string is commonly known as simple pendulum. The pendulum is made to oscillate back and forth by displacing the bob by a small angle θ from its equilibrium position and releasing it. In this experiment, you will employ a motion detector instead of a photo-gate used in the experiment 30.

II.   Equipment

Simple pendulum, photo-gates, computer, and motion detector

III.   Objectives

Part I   Investigate whether the motion of the simple pendulum is simple harmonic?

Part II   Study the dependence of the time period (T) on (1) angular amplitude, (2) mass of the bob, and (3) length

Part III   Investigate conservation of mechanical energy using simple pendulum

Part IV   Study damped oscillations using simple pendulum

IV. Experimental Details

Using PASCO Capstone/Datastudio Software

SET-UP

Open *DataStudio*, click on *create experiment* option. Attach the photo-gate to the projectile launcher, then plug the photo-gate into digital channel 1. Next plug the receptor panel to channel 2. Click *setup* button on the top left corner. Click *choose interface* button. Select *Science Workshop 500* interface. An image will now appear in the window. Select the left most yellow highlighted port (digital channel 1). Now select the "motion sensor" sensor option. Select the "motion sensor" tab option. Set the Standard Distance to 1m. Now close the experiment setup window. Now on the top left hand corner under "data" you should have position, velocity, and acceleration folders. When you are ready to start data collection hit the "start" button.

DATA ANALYSIS

In order to graph position, velocity, and acceleration you need to select the graph option under the displays menu of the bottom left hand corner. Select the run you want to graph under the parameter heading you want and hit ok. Then fit the graph with an appropriate curve.

The experimental arrangement is shown in Fig. 1. The motion detector should be approximately in The same plane as that of the oscillating simple pendulum. Adjust the height of the motion detector such that it is approximately at the same height as that of the simple pendulum bob when it is in equilibrium position. Keep the motion detector about ½ m away from the simple pendulum bob. Keep all the possible ultrasound reflectors away from the field of the detector except the bob of the simple pendulum so that you will not have spurious signals. Displace the bob in the plane of oscillation and release it. See that the simple pendulum oscillates in the plane with no jerks. You can judge this condition by collecting and plotting the data a couple of times making sure that there are no abrupt kinks or spikes particularly in the acceleration versus time graph. You adjust the position of the motion detector slightly while acquiring the data in the graph mode so that you can optimize the position of the motion detector to get best signals. By trial and error try to get the condition that the simple pendulum oscillates in a plane. After a couple of attempts, you should be able to get the condition that the simple pendulum oscillates in a plane. However if you find it difficult or time consuming to attain this condition, take two strings and tie them as shown in the Fig. 15.2. This arrangement should enable you to keep the oscillations of the simple pendulum in the plane more easily. Open the motion detector and collect the data for about 20 s at a sampling rate of 10-15 per second. Plot (a) displacement versus time, (b) velocity versus time, and (c) acceleration versus time graphs. Fit the curves to a sine function.

Part I
Is the motion of the simple pendulum simple harmonic?

The motion is said to be simple harmonic if the displacement can be represented by means of a sine function of single frequency. Give a small angular displacement of about 5° to the simple pendulum and collect the data for about 20 oscillations.

(Eq: 15.2) may be written in the form

$$m\frac{d^2s}{dt^2} = -mg\sin\theta = -mg\frac{s}{l}$$

$$\frac{d^2s}{dt^2} = \frac{g}{L}s \tag{15.10}$$

The solution of the differential equation may be written in the form

$$s(t) = s_0\sin(\omega t + \phi) \tag{15.11}$$

Where $s(t)$ is the displacement as a function of time, s_0 is the amplitude. ω is the angular frequency and φ is the phase. Fit the displacement versus time data to (Eq: 15.11). A good fit with R^2 deviation around 1 indicates that the periodic motion of the simple pendulum is simple harmonic.

Submit the plot with your lab report. The plot should have the fitted curve and the fitted parameters.

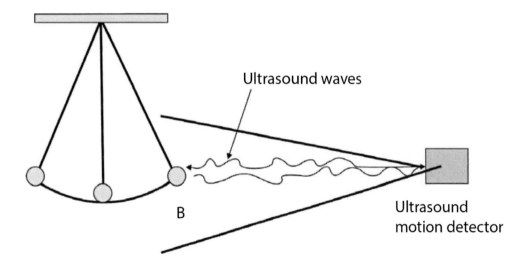

Figure 15.4 Experimental arrangement using a motion detector.

(a) Time period (T) is independent of the angular amplitude (for small angular amplitudes)

Measure the time periods of the simple pendulum for different angular amplitudes. Adjust the length of the simple pendulum to be approximately 1 m. Set the motion detector as shown in Fig. 15.4. Open the motion detector software and collect data for about 20 s at a sampling rate of 10 - 15 per sec. Plot a displacement versus time for different amplitudes say 3, 5, 8 and 10 cm. Fit the data to a sinusoidal function (Eq: 15.11)) and obtain the best fitted values of the amplitude S and the angular frequency ω. Calculate the time period $T = 2\pi/\omega$ and enter the data in *Table 15.5*.

Table 15.5: Time period versus angular amplitude.

Run #	Amplitude S from the computer fit (m)	Angular frequency ω from the computer fit (rad/s)	Time Period ($T = 2\pi/\omega$) (s)

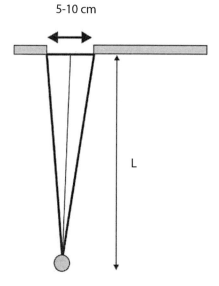

Figure 15.5: Simple Pendulum.

(b) The time period (T) is independent of the mass/material of the bob

Using bobs of different masses or of different materials, plot the displacement vs. time graph and obtain the corresponding time period (T) using the fit program. For all the measurements, keep the angular displacement small. For this part of the experiment, you will keep the length of the simple pendulum at some suitable value in the 60-100 cm range. Enter data in *Table 15.6*.

Table 15.6: The time period (T) is independent of the mass/material of the bob

Run #	Material of the bob	Mass of the bob	Angular frequency ω from the computer fit (rad/s)	Time Period (T =2π/ ω) (s)

(c) Time period (T) dependence on the length of the simple pendulum

At a given place, since the acceleration due to gravity is constant, the time period (*T*) is directly proportional to $\sqrt{L}$ where *L* is the length of the simple pendulum (Eq: 15.8). You would be interested in measuring the time period for about 4-5 values of the length. Select some convenient values for the length. For each length, collect the displacement versus time data for about 10-20 oscillations. Fit each of the plots to a sinusoidal equation of the type given by (Eq: 15.11). From the fits, obtain the angular frequency (*ω*) and calculate the time period (*T* = 2π/*ω*). Enter the data in *Table 15.3*. Make sure that the angular amplitude of the simple pendulum is small (3 -5 degrees). Transfer the data to an Excel spreadsheet and plot T^2 versus *L*. Fit the data to a linear function (*y* = m*x* + c). A good fit with R^2 deviation around 1 to a linear equation shows that T^2 is proportional to the length of the simple pendulum *L*. From the slope of the straight line, compute the value of the acceleration due to gravity (*g*).

Table 15.7: Time period versus length of the simple pendulum using a motion detector

Run #	Length of the pendulum *L* (m)	Angular frequency co from the computer fit (rad/s)	Time Period (*T* = 2π/ω) (s)	T^2 (s²)	T^2/L (s²/m)
1	0.7				
2	0.8				
3	0.9				
4	1.0				
5	1.1				
6	1.2				

Part II
Conservation of Mechanical Energy

Simple pendulum is a good example for the investigation of the conservation of mechanical energy. As the simple pendulum oscillates, when the bob is at the position B (Fig. (3)), the bob has a potential energy (= *mgh*) and the kinetic energy is zero. You can measure the potential energy with respect to any reference point. We choose the equilibrium position of the simple pendulum as the reference point. As the bob swings back and forth, the potential energy at B is converted to kinetic energy at the position A, which in turn is converted back to the potential energy at the position C. The simple pendulum has maximum potential energy and no kinetic energy at the positions B and C whereas it has maximum kinetic energy and no potential energy at the position A. This process keeps on repeating until the simple pendulum loses its energy due to the frictional and resistive forces. At intermediate positions between A and B, the simple pendulum will have intermediate values of both kinetic and potential energies. The mechanical energy of the system, that is, the sum of the potential and the kinetic energies, remains constant if we neglect the losses due to frictional and resistive forces.

For the calculation of the potential energy, take the equilibrium position of the bob as the reference point. If θ is the angular displacement (Fig. 3), the potential energy at the position B is = mgh = mgL (1 - cos θ).

Displace the bob of the simple pendulum such that the angular displacement is say 5° and release it. As the simple pendulum oscillates, collect data on displacement versus time for about 20 - 30 oscillations.

Potential energy of the bob as a function of time can be calculated as follows:

If s is the displacement of the bob from the mean position, the angular displacement

$$\theta \text{ (radians)} = s/L$$

The potential energy

$$mgh = mgL (1 - \cos \theta) \tag{15.12}$$

Fit the displacement versus time data to a sinusoidal equation (Eq. 15.11) and obtain the best-fitted values of the amplitude s. Fit the velocity versus time data to a sinusoidal function of the type

$$v(t) = v_0 \sin (\omega t + \varphi)$$

Obtain the maximum values of the velocity v_0 for each angle. Enter the data in an Excel spreadsheet and complete the calculations as shown in *Table 15.8*.

Table 15.8: Conservation of mechanical energy

Run #	Approx. θ measured using a protract or	Length of simple pendulum L	S_0	Angular displace-ment θ= S_0/L. (radians)	Mass of the bob m (kg)	PE (max) mgh = mgL (1-cosθ) (J)	Velocity (max) V_0 from computer fits(m/s)	KE (max) (½) mv_0^2 (J)	Total mechani-cal energy = KE+ME (J)

Transfer the data corresponding to (a) displacement versus time, (b) velocity versus time and (c) acceleration versus time to Excel spreadsheets. Using the displacement versus time data calculate the potential energy as a function of time using (Eq. 15.12). Calculate the kinetic energy as a function of time. Plot the potential energy versus time, kinetic energy versus time and the total mechanical energy versus time curves on the same plot.

Part III
Damped Oscillations

The amplitude of the oscillations decreases gradually because of the resistive forces due to air. You can investigate the effect of these drag forces by measuring the displacement versus time curve over an extended period of time. Collect the data for say 10 minutes (600 s) at a sampling rate of 5 per second. Fit the amplitudes versus time data to an exponential curve and calculate the drag constant.

V. Questions

1. Is there a phase difference in the (a) kinetic energy versus time and (b) potential energy versus time plots? If you did observe a phase difference, explain the physical significance of the observed phase difference. What phase difference do you expect? Is it in agreement with what you observed? Give your comments.

2. From the plot T^2 versus length (L), determine the slope of the curve and calculate the acceleration due to gravity.

3. In part 2 of the experiment, you investigated the time period versus angular displacement. Did you observe any systematic correlation between the time period (T) and the angular displacement?

4. For small amplitudes, we stated that the time period is independent of the angular amplitude. One student remarked that if the displacement is large, the bob travels longer distance and therefore the time period should increase with the increase of the amplitude. Give your response to her comment.

5. In this experiment, you are measuring the perpendicular distance traveled by the bob instead of the arc length you wish to measure. Does this introduce an error in your measurements and the calculations?

Advanced Level Experiments

Experiments 32, 33 & 34

I.   Introduction

In the previous Experiments 29 and 30, you have seen that for small amplitudes the simple pendulum executes simple harmonic motion. If the amplitude of the simple pendulum is not small, the oscillations of the simple pendulum is no more simple harmonic, it will contain higher harmonics of the fundamental frequency. In particular, the amplitude of the third harmonic of the fundamental will not be negligible and the time period will not be independent of the amplitude of the oscillations. In this experiment, you will investigate the effect of the higher harmonic components on the time period for large amplitude oscillations.

II.   Theory

(a) Small amplitude oscillations

A simple pendulum consists of a bob of mass m suspended from a fixed point by means of a mass less inextensible string. The bob is displaced by a small extent from its equilibrium position and released so that it oscillates back and forth about its equilibrium position. In this section we will investigate the motion of the simple pendulum when the angular amplitude (θ) of the oscillation is small.

Let θ be the angular displacement of the bob expressed in radians.

The length of the arc displaced $= L\theta$

Here L is the length of the simple pendulum measured from the point of suspension to the center of the bob.

The tangential velocity

$$v_r = L\frac{d\theta}{dt}$$

The tangential acceleration

$$a_r = L\frac{d^2\theta}{dt^2}$$

The forces acting on the bob at the position B are shown in Fig. 1. The gravitational force acts vertically downwards. The tension T is along the direction of the string upwards at an angle θ with respect to the vertical. We resolve the gravitational force mg into its components, one along the line of action of the tension and the other perpendicular to this, i.e., along the direction of the tangent at B as shown. Since there is no motion of the bob in the direction of the tension

$$+T - mg\cos\theta$$

The tangential component

$$F_t = -mg\sin\theta$$

is responsible for the tangential acceleration of the bob. According to Newton's second law

$$mL\frac{d^2\theta}{dt^2} = -mg\sin\theta \tag{1}$$

If is θ is small and expressed in radians $\sin\theta \sim \theta$

$$\ddot{\theta} = -\frac{g}{I}\theta \tag{2}$$

The solution for the angular displacement θ may be written in the form

$$\theta(t) = A\sin(\omega_o t + \phi) \tag{3}$$

The angular velocity

$$\theta(t) = -A\omega_0\cos(\omega_o t + \phi) \tag{4}$$

The angular acceleration

$$\ddot{\theta}(t) = -A\omega_0^2\sin(\omega_o t + \phi) \tag{5}$$

where A is the angular amplitude and ω_0 is the angular frequency. Substituting the values from (Eqs: 15.3 and 15.5) in (Eq. 15.2)

$$\omega_0^2 = \frac{g}{l} \quad \text{and} \quad \omega_0 = \sqrt{\frac{g}{L}} \tag{6}$$

the frequency

$$f_0 = \frac{1}{2\pi}\sqrt{\frac{g}{L}} \tag{7}$$

the time period

$$T = 2\pi\sqrt{\frac{L}{g}} \tag{8}$$

The constants A and φ are determined from the initial conditions, displacement and velocity at t = 0

$$(t) = A\sin(\omega_0 t + \phi)$$

$$\text{at } t = 0, \theta(t) = A \sin \phi \tag{9}$$

The angular velocity

$$\omega = \frac{d\theta(t)}{dt}$$

$$\omega = \dot{\theta}(t) = +\omega_0 A\cos(\omega_0 t + \phi)$$

$$\text{at } t = 0, \omega = +\omega_0 A\cos\phi \tag{10}$$

Solving (Eqs: 9 and 10), the two constants, i.e. the angular amplitude (A) and the phase (φ) can be calculated.

(b) Large angular displacements (anharmonic effects)

Let us consider the case when the angular displacement θ is not small. In this case, $\sin \theta$ cannot be approximated to θ. We use the expansion of $\sin \theta$ in terms of θ

$$\sin \theta = \theta - \frac{1}{6}\theta^3 + \frac{1}{120}\theta^5$$

We neglect the terms containing θ^5 and higher power terms, which are expected to be small compared to θ and θ^3 terms. The equation of motion (Eq. 1) may be written as

$$mL\ddot{\theta} = -mg\left[\theta - \frac{\theta^3}{6}\right] \tag{11}$$

$$\ddot{\theta} + \frac{g}{L}\left[\theta - \frac{\theta^3}{6}\right] = 0 \tag{12}$$

Substituting for the fundamental frequency

$$\omega_0 = \sqrt{\frac{g}{L}}$$

$$\ddot{\theta} + \omega_0^2\theta - \frac{\omega_0^2\theta^3}{6} = 0 \tag{13}$$

In the following, we present an approximate analytical solution. For additional details, the reader is referred to Kittel, Knight and Ruderman1.

We assume that the solution of Eq. (13) is a sine function of angular frequency ω and the third harmonic 3ω. Note that the angular frequency w may be different from the fundamental frequency ω.

$$\theta = A \sin \omega t + B \cos 3\omega t \tag{14}$$

$$\theta = A\omega \cos \omega t + 3B\omega \cos 3\omega t \tag{15}$$

$$\theta = A\omega^2 \sin \omega t - 9B\omega^2 \sin 3\omega t \tag{16}$$

Here, A and B are the angular amplitudes of the fundamental and the third harmonic respectively.

Substituting the values of θ and $d\theta/dt$ in (Eq. 13).

$$-A\omega \sin \omega t - 9B\omega^2 \sin 3\omega t + \omega_0^2 A \sin \omega t + \omega_0^2 B \sin 3\omega t$$

$$-\frac{\omega_0^2}{6}[A \sin \omega t + B \sin 3\omega t]^3 = 0 \tag{17}$$

Expanding the quantity in the parenthesis and retaining only the terms containing sin ωt

$$-A\omega \sin \omega t - 9B\omega^2 \sin 3\omega t + \omega_0^2 A \sin \omega t + \omega_0^2 B \sin 3\omega t - \frac{\omega_0^2}{6}[A^3 \sin^3 \omega t] = 0 \qquad (18)$$

Since

$$\sin^3 \omega t = \frac{3}{4}\sin \omega t - \frac{1}{4}\sin 3\omega t$$

may be written as

$$\frac{\omega_0^2}{6}\left[A^3\frac{3}{4}\sin \omega t - A^3\frac{1}{4}\right] = 0 \qquad (19)$$

The coefficient of sin wt and sin 3 ωt should vanish independently. The condition that sin cot should vanish gives

$$-\omega^2 A + \omega_0^2 A - \frac{\omega_0^2 A^3}{8} = 0$$

$$-\omega^2 + \omega_0^2 - \frac{1}{8}\omega_0^2 A^2 = 0$$

This gives

$$\omega^2 = \omega_0^2\left(1-\frac{1}{8}A^2\right)$$

$$\omega = \omega_0\left(1-\frac{1}{8}A^2\right)^{1/4}$$

Expanding this equation and neglecting the higher order terms

$$\omega = \omega_0\left(1-\frac{1}{16}A^2\right) \qquad (20)$$

This expression gives the dependence of co on A. As A→0, ω →ω0 as expected.

$$\omega = 2\pi f = \omega_0 \left(1 - \frac{1}{16}A^2\right)$$

$$f = \frac{1}{2\pi}\sqrt{\frac{g}{L}}\left(1 - \frac{1}{16}A^2\right) \tag{21}$$

$$T = 2\pi\sqrt{\frac{L}{g}}\left(1 - \frac{1}{16}A^2\right)^{-1}$$

$$T = 2\pi\sqrt{\frac{L}{g}}\left(1 + \frac{1}{16}A^2\right) \tag{22}$$

$$\frac{T - T_0}{T_0} \approx \frac{1}{16}A^2 \tag{23}$$

where T_0 is the time period corresponding to the fundamental frequency

$$T_0 = \frac{1}{2\pi}\sqrt{\frac{L}{g}}$$

For an angular displacement of 30° corresponding to 0.524 radians, the fractional change in the angular frequency

$$\frac{\omega - \omega_0}{\omega_0} = \frac{\Delta\omega}{\omega_0} = -\frac{1}{16}A^2 = -0.017$$

This corresponds to a fractional decrease in frequency of 1.7%. For an angular displacement of 450 corresponding to 0.79 radians, the fractional decrease in the frequency is 3.9%. Here, one would notice that the frequency decreases with the increase in the angular displacement. The time period correspondingly increases with the increase in the angular displacement. For an angular displacement of 300, the increase in the time period T is 1.7%. Since one could measure the time period to third or fourth decimal place using a photo-gate arrangement, the changes in the time period can be measured easily.

Equating the coefficient of sin $3\omega t = 0$, we get

$$-9\omega^2 B + \omega_0^2 B + \frac{\omega_0^2 A^3}{24} = 0$$

Since ω is of the order of ω_0, Putting $\omega^2 = \omega_0^2$

$$-9\omega_0^2 B + \omega_0^2 B + \frac{\omega_0^2 A^3}{24} = 0$$

Since $\omega^2 \neq 0$,

$$-8B = -\frac{A^3}{24}$$

$$\frac{B}{A} = \frac{A^2}{192} \tag{24}$$

For $A \approx 0.3$ rad, we have $(B/A) = 4.7 \times 10^{-4}$ which is quite small. (B/A) gives the fractional shift mixture of sin $3\omega t$ to sin ωt term. This justifies the fact that we could neglect the higher order terms in sin $3\omega t$ and also products (sin^2 ωt x sin 3 ωt) in Eq. (17).

For $= 45^0 = 0.785$ radian

$B/A = 3.2 \times 10^{-3}$

If the amplitude of the simple pendulum is large, the simple pendulum will have multiple frequencies. The most dominant term ω_0 corresponds to the fundamental frequency. In addition to the strong fundamental, it will also have the third harmonic corresponding to the term sin 3 ωt. The amplitude of the third harmonic is quite small compared to the fundamental. The ratio of the third harmonic component to the fundamental (B/A) is given by Eq. (24)

III. Experimental

Measure the time period (T) as a function of the angular displacement (θ) and compare the experimental values with the calculated ones using the (Eq: 23). Enter the data in Table 1.

Keep the length of the simple pendulum about 70 - 100 cm. Arrange the photo-gate at the mean position of the simple pendulum. Displace the bob by an angular displacement θ and measure the angle using a protractor and release the bob. Make sure the string is taut when you release the bob. Measure the time period using the photo-gate.

Using Datastudio Software

SET-UP

Open *DataStudio*, click on *create experiment* option. Attach the photo-gate to the projectile launcher, then plug the photo-gate into digital channel 1. Next plug the receptor panel to channel 2. Click *setup* button on the top left corner. Click choose *interface* button. Select *Science Workshop* 500 interface. An image will now appear in the window. Select the left most yellow highlighted port (digital channel 1). Now select the "photo-gate and pendulum" sensor option. Now close the experiment setup window. Now on the top left hand corner under "data" you should have a folder for "period" and one for "velocity". When you are ready to start data collection hit the "start" button.

DATA ANALYSIS

In order to graph the period you need to select the graph option under the displays menu of the bottom left hand corner. Select whichever run you want to measure under the specific folder and hit ok.

Table 1: Anharmonic effects in the time period
of a simple pendulum having large angular displacements.

Time period of the simple pendulum for small angular amplitude $(T_0) = \quad$ s

Run #	Length of the simple pendulum (m)	Angular displacement θ (degrees)	Angular displacement θ in (radians)	Time for 50 oscillations (s)	Time period (T)	$((T-T_0)/T_0) = \Delta T/T_0$	θ^2 (radians)^2
1	1	3 cm					
2	1	5 cm					
3	1	10 cm					
4	1	15 cm					
5	1	20 cm					
6	1	25 cm					
7	1	30 cm					
8	1	35 cm					
9	1	40 cm					

Plot $(\Delta T/T_0)$ vs. A^2. Fit the data to a linear equation. Obtain the slope of the curve from the best fits. The expected value of the slope is $= 1/16$. Compare your measured value with the expected value. Calculate the % accuracy. A straight-line curve fit with a slope of $\sim(1/16)$ proves the relation given by (Eq: 23)

References

1. C. Kittel, W. D. Knight and M. A. Ruderman, *Mechanics, Berkeley Physics Course, Vol. 1*, McGraw Hill Publishing Co., 1962, pp. 192-199.

2. A. P. Arya, *Introduction to Classical Mechanics*, Allyn and Bacon, 1990, pp. 336-339.

I.   Introduction and Objectives

In experiment 28, you investigated the simple harmonic motion of a mass attached to a spring. In that experiment the amplitude of the oscillations remained approximately constant over the time period you have studied which is of the order of 10 s. The amplitude remained constant because the air resistance to the motion of the mass is small and the frictional forces of the spring are negligible. As you know, over larger times of observation, the amplitude of the oscillation gradually reduces ultimately to zero. If you collect data over a period say 30 minutes (1800 s), you would notice that the amplitude of the oscillations decreases gradually as a function of time. The amplitude of the oscillation decreases because of the drag force, which opposes the motion of the object. The energy of the harmonic oscillator gradually decreases and the energy lost is converted primarily to thermal energy of the air. The drag force is always directed opposite to the direction of motion of the object.

Objective

To (1) investigate the affect of the drag force on the oscillations of a mass attached to a spring and (2) measure the damping constants of different media.

SIMPLE HARMONIC OSCILLATOR

Consider a mass m attached to a spring of spring constant k. Let the mass m be on a frictionless horizontal surface. If we stretch the spring horizontally and release it, the mass executes oscillatory motion about its mean position (Fig.1). The displacement x is measured from its equilibrium position.

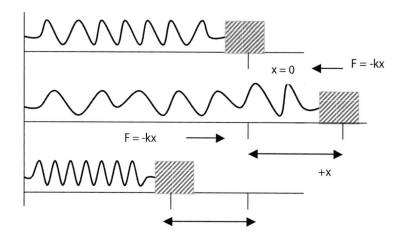

Figure 1 Horizontal oscillations of a spring.

According to the Hooke's law,

$$F_x = -kx \qquad (1)$$

From the Newton's second law

$$F(x) = ma = m\frac{d^2x}{dt^2}$$

Assuming the spring is of negligible mass

$$m\frac{d^2x}{dt^2} = -kx$$

$$\frac{d^2x}{dt^2} + \frac{k}{m}x = 0 \qquad (2)$$

Which is the equation of a simple harmonic motion. The solution may be written in the form

$$x = A\cos(\omega_0 t + \phi) \qquad (3)$$

Where A is the amplitude and φ is the phase constant. The values of A and φ can be determined from the initial conditions. The velocity

$$v(t) = \frac{dx}{dt} = \dot{x} = -A\omega_0 \sin(\omega_0 t + \phi) \qquad (4)$$

and the acceleration

$$a(t) = \frac{d^2x}{dt^2} = \ddot{x} = -A\omega^2 \cos(\omega_0 t + \phi)$$

resulting

$$\ddot{x} + \omega_0^2 x = 0 \tag{6}$$

Comparing Eqs. (2) and (6) we get

$$\omega_0 = \sqrt{\frac{k}{m}} \tag{7}$$

The motion is simple harmonic with an angular frequency $\omega 0$. Since the sine and cosine differ by a phase of $\pi/2$, you notice from equations (3) and (4) the displacement and velocity are out of phase by $\pi/2$. The amplitude and phase are determined from the displacement (x) and the velocity (dx/dt) at the initial condition t = 0.

The displacement

$$x = A \cos(\omega_0 t + \phi)$$

at t = 0,

$$x = A \cos\phi \tag{8}$$

The velocity v(t)

$$v = \dot{x} = -A\omega_0 \sin(\omega_0 t + \phi) \tag{9}$$

at t = 0,

$$v_0 = -A\omega_0 \sin\phi$$

The acceleration

$$a(t) = \ddot{x} = -A\omega_0 \cos(\omega_0 t + \phi)$$

$$a(t = 0) = -A\omega_0 \cos\phi \tag{10}$$

The acceleration is out of phase with respect to the displacement by π.

The displacement, velocity and acceleration for different values of angular frequency, amplitude and phase constant can be calculated and plotted easily using the electronic spreadsheets.

Damped Harmonic Oscillator

We will investigate the effect of a damping force on the motion of a simple harmonic oscillator. The damping can be due to the resistive forces offered by the spring or the resistive forces offered by air opposing the motion of the mass attached to the spring. Let us assume that the spring is of light mass and the resistive forces of the spring can be neglected. In the following, we consider the effect of the resistive forces on the motion of the mass. If the speed of the mass is small, the damping force is proportional to the magnitude of the velocity and is opposite in direction.

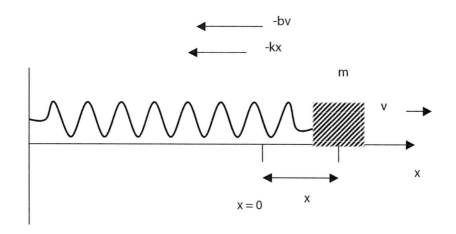

Figure 2

The restoring force of the spring

$$F_{spring} = -kx$$

The drag force is proportional to the velocity and is oppositely directed,

$$F_{drag} = -bv = -b\dot{x} \tag{11}$$

From the Newton's second law, the equation of motion may be written as

$$m\ddot{x} = b\dot{x} + kx = 0 \tag{12}$$

which is a second order differential equation. Rewriting this equation,

$$\ddot{x} + \frac{b}{m}\dot{x} + \frac{k}{m}x = 0$$

We substitute

$$\tau = \frac{b}{2m} \qquad \text{and} \qquad \omega_0^2 = \frac{k}{m} \tag{13}$$

$$\ddot{x} + 2\tau \dot{x} + \omega_0^2 x = 0 \tag{14}$$

We assume a solution of the type

$$x = e^{\lambda t} \tag{15}$$

$$\dot{x} = \lambda e^{\lambda t}$$

$$\ddot{x} = \lambda^2 e^{\lambda t}$$

Substituting these values in Eq. (14)

$$\lambda^2 e^{\lambda t} + 2\tau \lambda e^{\lambda t} + \omega_0^2 e^{\lambda t} = 0$$

$$e^{\lambda t}(\lambda^2 + 2\tau \lambda + \omega_0^2) = 0$$

Since $x = e^{\lambda t}$ is finite and not equal to zero, the quantity within the parenthesis should be equal to zero.

$$\lambda^2 + 2\tau \lambda + \omega_0^2 = 0 \tag{16}$$

The roots of this equation are

$$\lambda = \frac{-2\tau \pm \sqrt{4\lambda^2 - 4\omega_0^2}}{2}$$

Let

$$\lambda_1 = -\tau + \sqrt{\lambda^2 - \omega_0^2} \tag{17}$$

$$\lambda_2 = -\tau - \sqrt{\lambda^2 - \omega_0^2} \tag{18}$$

The general solution may be written in the form

$$x(t) = Ae^{\lambda_1 t} + Be^{\lambda_2 t} \tag{19}$$

Substituting λ1 and λ2 from Eqs. (17) and (18) in Eq. (19), we get

$$x(t) = e^{-\tau t}\left[Ae^{+\sqrt{\tau^2 - \omega_0^2}\,t} + Be^{+\sqrt{\tau^2 - \omega_0^2}\,t}\right]$$

(20)

Where A and B are constants.

There are three special cases of interest

a. **Lightly damped** ($\omega_{20} > \tau_2$)
b. **Critically damped** ($\omega_{20} = \tau_2$)
c. **Heavily damped** ($\omega_{20} < \tau_2$)

In the following, we will discuss these cases in greater detail

a. **Underdamped** (Lightly damped) motion. We define

$$\omega_1^2 = \omega_0^2 - \tau^2 = \frac{k}{m} - \frac{b^2}{4m^2}$$

(21)

$$\omega_1 = \pm\left[\frac{k}{m} - \frac{b^2}{4m^2}\right]^{1/2}$$

Expressing the roots in the imaginary form, Eq. (21) may be written in the form

$$i^2\,\omega_1^2 = \tau^2 - \omega_0^2 \quad and \quad i\,\omega_1 = \sqrt{\tau^2 - \omega_0^2}$$

Putting these values in Eq. (20), we get

$$x(t) = e^{-\tau t}(Ae^{i\,\omega_1 t}\,Be^{-i\,\omega_1 t})$$

(22)

$$e^{\pm i\,\omega_1 t} = \cos\omega_1 t \pm i\sin\omega_1^2$$

Eq. (22) may be written in the form

$$x(t) = e^{-\tau t}[(A+B)\cos\omega_1 t + i(A-B)\sin\omega_1 t]$$

(23)

If we put $(A + B) = C$ and $i(A - B) = D$

The solution $x(t)$ may be written in the form

$$x(t) = e^{-\tau t}[C\cos\omega_1 t + D\sin\omega_1 t] \tag{23}$$

Writing

$$x_{\text{max}} = \sqrt{C^2 + D^2}$$

$$x(t) = Ae^{-\tau t}\cos(\omega_1 t + \phi) \tag{24}$$

The phase

$$\phi = \tan^{-1}(C/D)$$

ω_1 is commonly known as the angular frequency of the damped oscillator. It should be noted that the motion is not strictly periodic since the sinusoidal function is multiplied by a time dependent exponential function.

If the damping term is small $\tau \to 0$

$$\omega_1 = \sqrt{\omega_0^2 + \tau^2} \approx \omega_0 \tag{25}$$

As expected. The frequency of the anharmonic oscillator is equal to the fundamental frequency.

Note that the frequency of the damped oscillator (ω_1) is less than that of the undamped oscillator ($\omega 0$). The amplitude of the damped oscillator decreases exponentially because of the $e^{-\tau t}$ factor. The envelope of the amplitude versus time curve is given by

$$x_{\text{envelope}} = \pm Ae^{-\tau t} \tag{26}$$

The amplitude of the oscillations decreases exponentially (Eq. 26).

(b) Critically damped case is of particular interest $\tau^2 = \omega_0^2$

In this case

$$\lambda_1 = \lambda_2 = -\tau$$

The solution may be written in the form

$$x(t) = Ce^{-\tau t}$$

The general solution may be written as

$$x(t) = (C_1 + C_2 t)e^{-\tau t} \tag{27}$$

where C1 and C2 are constants which can be determined from the initial conditions.

(c) Heavily damped

The two roots given by equations (17) and (18) are real

Putting

$$(\lambda_2 - \omega_0^2)^{1/2} = \omega_2$$

The solution for x(t) given by Eq. (22) may be written as

$$x(t) = e^{-\tau t}\left[Ae^{\omega_2 t} + Be^{-\omega_2 t}\right]$$

The displacement will not have oscillatory behavior but reaches the zero value asymptotically.

Experimental

Suspend the spring vertically and attach a weight hanger. Add   additional weights of about 50 g to the hanger so that the spring is stretched within its elastic limit and there are no kinks. Attach a cardboard to the spring just above the weights so that the ultrasound waves are reflected from the cardboard back to the ultrasound detector.

1.   Measure the value of the fundamental frequency (ω_0) by setting the mass in oscillation by gently lifting it upwards and releasing it.   Using the motion detector measure the displacement as a function of time and fit the data to a sinusoidal function to get the best-fitted value of the fundamental angular frequency (ω_0).

Using Datastudio Software

SET-UP

Open *DataStudio*, click on *create experiment* option. Plug the yellow wire of the motion sensor into digital channel 1, and the black wire into digital channel 2. Click setup button on the top left corner. Click choose interface button. Select Science Workshop 500 interface. An image will now appear in the window. Select the left most yellow highlighted port (digital channel 1). Now select the "motion sensor" sensor option. Select the "motion sensor" tab option. Set the Standard Distance to 1m. Now close the experiment setup window. Now on the top left hand corner under "data" you should have position, velocity, and acceleration folders. When you are ready to start data collection hit the "start" button.

DATA ANALYSIS

In order to graph position you need toselect the graph option under the displays menu of the bottom left hand corner. Select the run you want to graph under the parameter heading and hit ok. Then fit the graph with an appropriate curve.

(a) Lightly damped

Oscillations of the mass in air would provide the data for lightly damped case. The resistance due to air provides the drag force. Collect the displacement versus time data for the mass oscillating in air for about 10- 20 minutes (600- 1200 s) at a low sampling rate of (5 samples /s). You notice that the amplitude of the oscillations decreases exponentially with time. Fit the data to Eq. (24) and obtain the best values of τ and ω_1.

(b) Moderately damped

Immerse the weight in a light fluid such as kerosene or turpentine. Keep the beaker on an adjustable lab jack and adjust the height of the jack such that the weights are immersed in the fluid. You would notice that the displacement reaches zero much faster than the lightly damped case. Start the motion detector and collect data on displacement versus time for 3-4 minutes. Fit the data to Eq. (24) and obtain the best values of τ and ω_1.

(c) Heavily damped

Immerse the weights in glycerin and displace the mass downward by gently pushing the cardboard downward and releasing it. This will be the case for overdamped motion and the displacement reaches zero value asymptotically. In this case, the solution for displacement does not result in an oscillatory behavior. Fit the data to Eq. (27) and obtain the best-fitted values of τ and ω_2

Table 1: Damped Harmonic Oscillator

Damping	Angular frequency	τ	ω_0^2	$\tau2$	ω_0^2/τ^2
Undamped (air)	ω_0				
Lightly damped (air)	ω_1				
Moderately damped (turpentine)	ω_1				
Heavily damped (glycerin)	ω_2				

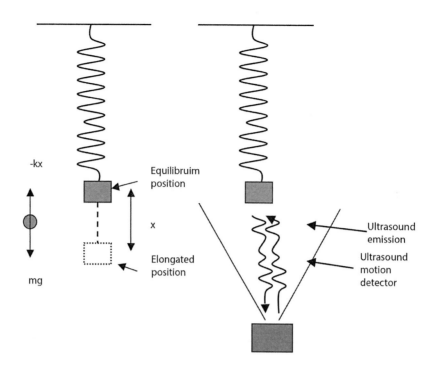

References

2. J. B. Marion, *Classical Dynamics of Particles and Systems*, Academic Press, 1970, p. 101 – 106.

3. A. P. Arya, *Introduction to Classical Mechanics*, Prentice Hall, 1990, p. 63-72.

4. C. Kittel, W. D. Knight and M. A. Ruderman, Mechanics, *Berkeley Physics Course*, Volume 1, McGrawHill Publishing Co., 1962. p 207-220.

EXPERIMENT 34

LONGITUDINAL OSCILLATIONS OF TWO COUPLED MASSES

I.   Introduction and Objectives

The experimental arrangement is shown in Fig.1. The two gliders represented by m glide on an air track where the frictional forces are small and can be neglected. Let the masses of the gliders be equal to m. Let the springs— S_1, S_2, and S_3— be identical, each of spring constant k. Let the masses of the springs be small compared to the masses of the gliders. In the following discussion, we neglect the masses of the springs.

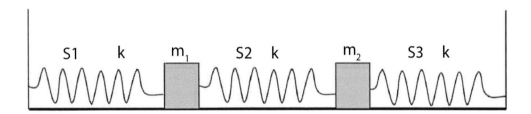

Figure 1

When a system oscillates in harmonic motion, it is called a mode. I n this case, since there are two masses, there will be two degrees of freedom, and hence, two modes. Therefore, each mode will have a well-defined force constant and hence a unique frequency of oscillation.

Symmetric Mode

Let us displace the masses 1 and 2 by the same amount to the right, starting from their equilibrium positions.

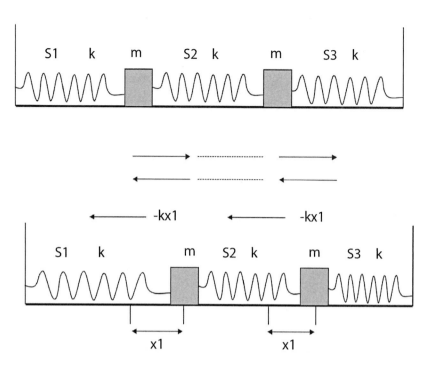

Springs S1, S2, and S3 are identical The masses $m_1 = m_2 = m$

Figure 2: Two harmonic oscillators coupled together by three springs.
The masses are displaced to the right in a symmetric mode.

The elongation of S_1 is equal to the compression o f S_3. S_2 will be unaffected and its length will be the same as in the unstretched position and therefore it will not exert any force on either of the masses. The mass, m_1, will be pulled left by the spring S_1 with a force $= - k\, x_1$. The mass, m_2, will be pushed towards the left by the spring, S_3, with an equal force $= -k\, x_1$.

Both m_1 and m_2 will oscillate with an angular frequency.

$$\omega_1 = \sqrt{\frac{k}{m}} \tag{1}$$

In the symmetric mode, the two masses oscillate in phase at their original frequencies as if there is no coupling between them.

Antisymmetric Mode

We will displace the two masses by the same amount but in opposite directions. Let us assume that we move m1 to the right by x_1 and m_2 to the left by $- x_2$. Mass m_1 will experience two forces. Spring S_1 pulling towards left with a force of $= - kx_2$. The spring S_2 that is compressed by $2x_2$, will be pushing m_1 with a force of $- 2kx_2$ again towards the left. The net force on m_1 will be $= - 3kx_2$

The angular frequency of m_1 will be

$$\omega_2 = \sqrt{\frac{3k}{m}} = \sqrt{3}\,\omega_1 \tag{2}$$

The mass m_2 will experience a force of $-2k_2$ due to spring S_2 and $-kx_1$ due to spring S_3. The net force acting on m_2 will be $= -3kx_2$.

The angular frequency of m_2 will be

$$\omega_2 = \sqrt{\frac{3k}{m}} = \sqrt{3}\,\omega_1$$

Same as that of m_1

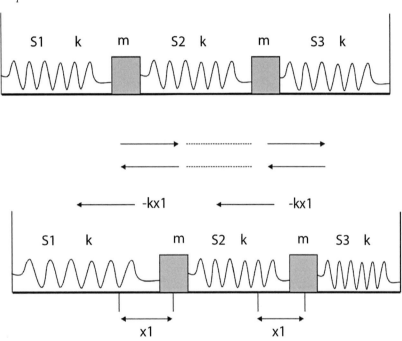

Figure 3: Two harmonic oscillators coupled by means of three springs.
The oscillators are in the anharmonic mode.

Thus, in the anti-symmetric mode, masses m_1 and m_2 oscillate out of phase and their frequency is higher than their individual uncoupled frequency. In the anti-symmetric mode, since the symmetry is destroyed, you need higher energy thus an increasing frequency compared to the symmetric mode.

II.   Theory

The equation of motion for mode 1 is

$$m\frac{d^2x_1}{dt^2} = -kx_1 \tag{3}$$

The solution may be written as

$$x_1(t) = A\cos(\omega_1 t + \phi_1) \tag{4}$$

where A is the amplitude and φ_1 is the phase. The angular frequency ω_1 is given by (Eq. 1) The equation of motion for mode 2 may be written as

$$m\frac{d^2x_2}{dt^2} = -3kx_2 \tag{5}$$

The solution may be written as

$$x_2(t) = B\cos(\omega_2 t + \phi_2) \tag{6}$$

The angular frequency, ω_2, is given by Eq. (2).

III.   Experimental

Level the air track to be horizontal using a level indicator. Adjust the airflow such that the gliders are moving friction free. Arrange the spring and the gliders as shown in Fig. 1. Gliders serve as the harmonic oscillators of mass m. Fix a flag on one of the gliders so that ultrasound waves may be reflected from the flag and detected by the ultrasound detector. Make sure that the signals you are getting are from the flag and not from the objects nearby. You may test this condition by moving the glider at different speeds manually and monitoring the signals from the motion detector.

IV.   Procedure

Using Datastudio Software

SET-UP

Open *DataStudio*, click on *create experiment* option. Plug the yellow wire of the motion sensor into digital channel 1, and the black wire into digital channel 2. Click setup button on the top left corner. Click choose interface button. Select *Science Workshop* 500 interface. An image will now appear in the window. Select the left most yellow highlighted port (digital channel 1). Now select the "motion sensor" sensor option. Select the "motion sensor" tab option. Set the Standard Distance to 1m. Now close the experiment setup window. Now on the top left hand corner under "data" you should have position, velocity, and acceleration folders. When you are ready to start data collection hit the "start" button.

DATA ANALYSIS

In order to graph position you need toselect the graph option under the displays menu of the bottom left hand corner. Select the run you want to graph under the parameter heading and hit ok. Then fit the graph with an appropriate curve.

Symmetric Mode

Hold m_1 and m_2 at their equilibrium positions and pull them by displacing them by equal amounts in the same direction and releasing them simultaneously. Collect data corresponding to displacement versus time using the motion detector. Fit the data to a sine function and obtain the value of the angular frequency, ω1.

Antisymmetric Mode

Hold m_1 and m_2 at their equilibrium positions, pull them equally in opposite directions, and release them simultaneously. Collect data corresponding to displacement versus time using the motion detector. Fit the data to a sine function and obtain the value of the angular frequency, ω_2. Compare the value of the measured angular frequency ω_2 with the expected value $\sqrt{3}\,\omega_1$.

In general, you will find that both symmetric and antisymmetric modes are present in both of the cases studied above. You can find the relative intensities of these modes using Fourier analysis of the data. The Fourier analysis technique separates the frequency components and allows plotting the amplitude and intensity of the frequency components ω_1 and ω_2 separately.

Repeat the experiment for three sets of equal masses ($m_1 = m_2 = m$). You can change the mass of the gliders by putting additional weights symmetrically on both sides of the glider. When you put additional weights, make sure that the air pressure is adequate and the gliders slide without friction.

V.   Questions

1.   Find the modes and the corresponding frequencies for coupled masses each of mass m and the springs S_1 and S_3 coupled as shown in Fig. 4.

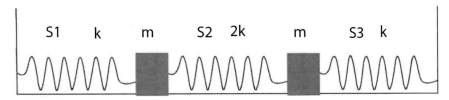

Figure 4

2.   Two identical springs of spring constant k are stretched from their equilibrium positions and connected to a mass m as shown in Fig. 5 on an air track, where the frictional forces are small and can be neglected. If the mass is displaced to t he right by x, find the frequency of oscillation of the mass, m.

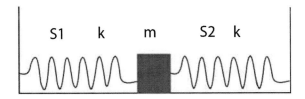

Figure 5